Spilling Ink: Volume 1

A Collection of Fiction, Nonfiction and Prose Poetry

Other Works Published by Unbound Press

Anthologies

By Invitation Only
Loose Leaves

Nonfiction

Circe's Island by Isabel Gillard
Scottish Wedding Planner by Nicola Taylor

Novels

Annabel by Elon Whittaker
French Sally by William Prince
Unreasonable Force by Charlie Taylor
Year of the Ginkgo by Sharon Dilworth

Short Story Collections

The Journey and Other Stories by Charlie Taylor
That's What Ya Get! Kowalski's Assertions by
Brindley Hallam Dennis

www.unboundpress.com

Spilling Ink: Volume 1

A Collection of Fiction, Nonfiction and Prose Poetry

Cၛྵ

Edited and with a Foreword by

Amy Burns

Published by Unbound Press

Spilling Ink: Volume 1

First published in 2011 by Unbound Press
1/1, 308 Clyde Street
Glasgow, G1 4NP
www.unboundpress.com

In association with

Spilling Ink Review
www.spillinginkreview.com

Unbound Press & Spilling Ink Review - divisions of
Arts Unbound Limited
Registered Offices: 123 Wellington Road South, Stockport, SK1
3TH

ISBN 978-0-9568519-0-1

Printed in the United Kingdom & United States of America
Typeset & Cover Design by Amy Burns

I urge you to please notice when you are happy, and exclaim or murmur or think at some point, "If this isn't nice, I don't know what is."

Kurt Vonnegut

Contents

☙

Fiction

Nonfiction

Prose Poetry

100 Words or Less

Foreword

❧

To authors who 'wonder and worry' about the 'interrelation between a writer and the nation or universal community,' Vladimir Nabokov recommended the 'much abused ivory tower.' But Nabokov continued:

> There is a lot to be said for mingling now and then with the crowd, and he must be a pretty foolish and short-sighted author who renounces the treasures of observation, humour, and pity which may be professionally obtained through closer contact with his fellow men.

How about closer contact with his fellow writers? Fellow readers? And in my case, fellow editors? I think this anthology provides a wonderful opportunity for 'mingling' in the Nabokovian sense. And yes, he *is* turning over in his grave as I type; such liberties won't go down well I'm afraid. It's a good thing that I don't have a problem with irascible ghosts.

Spilling Ink: Volume 1 is particularly special to me not only because it represents our first year of hard work at *Spilling Ink Review* but also because it represents twelve months of publishing excellent fiction, nonfiction and prose poetry, building relationships with international authors, and awarding hundreds of pounds to our competition winners. Contained within these pages are the winners and short-listed entries from our literary competitions. It takes a great leap of faith to send off a competition entry fee to a start-up like *Spilling Ink Review*. I hope that this anthology serves as a positive example that some people do keep their word; some people do care. I am particularly grateful to those who took a chance, exercised a little faith and sent something much more precious than money: the product of their craft.

Alongside our competition winners you'll also find particularly excellent works that we've published throughout the year in

Spilling Ink online. Read on for fiction of drastically varied styles and lengths; from short stories, flash fictions, to micro-bursts of 100 words or less. Read on for thought-provoking creative nonfiction; from commentary on the micro-dynamics of personal relationships to the macro-dynamics of social and political unrest. Read on for evocative prose poetry; from Scottish dialect to Manhattan rooftops. Read on and I hope that you find as much pleasure in reading as I found in publishing this collection of *Spilling Ink's* best-of-the-best.

Amy Burns

Fiction

ॐ

I write entirely to find out what I'm thinking, what I'm looking at, what I see and what it means. What I want and what I fear.

Joan Didion

Gills

Rosie Adams

CБ

Your mum has gills on her neck but it's not a big deal. She doesn't usually need to use them during the week and she wears colourful scarves outdoors so most people don't know. But sometimes, on a Wednesday or Thursday if she's doing the washing up, she might plunge her head into the sink and refuse to emerge, even when you yank so hard at her shirt collar that it rips off and you have to stuff it down the back of the sofa in case she realises later and gives you a slap. On the weekends she stays in the bath all day. She doesn't hear or feel anything when she's under water. You can turn the TV up till the neighbours bang on the walls, run around with no clothes on, pull all the tape out of her cassettes – she won't notice. But those things get boring. Mostly, on Saturdays, you sit on the toilet, watching her hair flutter around her shoulders, her breasts bobbing like buoys, hoping that by some miracle she'll wake up early and take you to Laser Quest.

Breakfast

Viccy Adams

ભ્ર

Hanging on the wall in the hallway of my parents' house is a portrait of my great grandparents on their engagement day. It's one of those typical, non-smiling sepia photographs. He has a massive moustache and her hair is scraped back off her face so hard it must have been painful.

They're both facing slightly off centre. One of his hands is blurred; it looks as if he moved it from resting on her shoulder to cupping her elbow. Or the other way round. I've walked past it a thousand times without ever really stopping to look.

My mother puts her hand on my shoulder and pushes me closer.

"Recognise that brooch?" she asks. I shake my head. "I wore it last time you visited. Last summer."

I feel bad about not recognising the brooch. The gilt on the wooden frame is chipped. I tell my mother she looks like her grandfather.

"All us Gordonstouns have that chin. You should look in the mirror more."

"I'm scared that this is going to cause problems between you, dad and me." I look at my feet. I don't want to see the disappointment in her eyes.

"My grandmother's name was Lily. She was listening to details of the Armistice declaration on the radio and twisting the engagement ring on her finger when the postman knocked on the door. Lily answered the door, collected the day's post and left it on the kitchen table while she made breakfast.

"Then Lily sat down to eat her toast and look through the mail. She was wondering whether she should wear her sister's wedding dress, new five years before, or alter her mother's.

"The letter from her fiancé's commanding officer was short, but Lily let her breakfast grow cold while reading it over and over again. By the time someone found her, the cup of tea had a film on it, the eggs were congealed and the letter was transparent with tears.

"For a good six months, Lily refused to leave the house. She wore only black and set her lips in a thin, pale line when people spoke to her. She sat and twisted the engagement ring round her finger while the spring happened to other people, outside. Left in the house alone, she drew the curtains and wept.

"One morning, Lily was up early and scrubbing the kitchen step by the half-dawn light. The postman limped up the path and crouched down next to her.

'Let's talk,' said the postman. Lily made him a cup of tea. They talked for an hour and he was late for work. The next day Lily had the kettle on the hob when he arrived. The day after, she waited inside, in her good dress rather than her housework clothes.

"By the end of a fortnight, Lily started talking to her family again. Just the odd remark, about the weather and such like. After a month, the postman was coming in for breakfast and Lily was wearing a green skirt.

"The other soldiers came home from the war and the first time Lily saw a uniform on the street, she burst into tears and had to be taken into the back room of the bakery to sit down.

"Later that same day, Lily tied up a bundle of letters and mementoes with some ribbon. She put the bundle in an empty biscuit tin and put the engagement ring on top, wrapped in a leftover scrap of velvet. Then she put the lid on the biscuit tin and put it away in the farthest corner of the top shelf of the linen cupboard.

"Lily and the postman got engaged at the height of summer."

"What did they talk about?" I ask. My mother turns away from the photograph to look at me.

"He felt terribly guilty."

"About her fiancé?"

"He was lame from birth. He didn't see active service. Instead he brought bad news. That's what my grandmother always said. He felt like a storm crow. Loving my grandmother was a sort of apology."

"What about her? Did she love him?" My mother points at Lily's brooch.

"He gave it to her as a love token, when they started courting officially. She wore it until the day she died."

"Two days before the wedding, the postman knocked on the door and Lily answered it with a smile. She was wearing a green ribbon in her hair. He gave her a flower and a handful of letters. She gave him a kiss for each hour left before the church ceremony.

"Mainly the letters were typewritten bills for the wedding preparations. One was handwritten. Lily didn't recognise the handwriting, a fact she never admitted to anyone because it was the deepest cut of shame.

"After Lily read the handwritten letter, she went upstairs to the linen closet and took out the biscuit tin and took the old engagement ring out of the scrap of velvet."

We stand in silence, both looking at the photograph.

"I found her diary when my parents moved across here, to the East coast. I don't think anyone else has ever read it. Turned out the first fiancé hadn't been killed at all; he was a P.O.W., held in an internment camp in Switzerland. His parents didn't approve of the engagement. When they received a telegram informing them that he was still alive, Lily was already stepping out with the postman. They kept it a secret from everyone."

"What did she do?"

"There was a massive scandal. Lily and her husband had to move from Aberdeen to Ayr to escape it."

"Who did she marry?"

"Neither of them. She called off both engagements and married one of the baker's sons. William Gordonstoun. Her parents stood by her."

I digest this in silence while we walk back through to the kitchen, where my father is washing the breakfast dishes.

My father hands me a tea-towel and I dry while my mother waters the houseplants.

Outside, the sun streams down on the snow and everything is ringing with light.

The Stench of Strangers

Christina Brooks

ॐ

At first it felt like any other Saturday morning as I returned home from perusing antiques in the Portabella road. I parked my mini in the driveway and locked the car door. I looked up at my house as I had done a thousand times before, but this time something was different. The bedroom window was open and the curtains were flailing over the sill, flapping against the brickwork like fish tails smacking in wet sands. My heart began to quicken as I made my way to the front door.

Stepping into the cool azure hallway, I moved from the reality of suburban London into a dream. The once familiar territory of my home was now unfamiliar and, as I slumped against the walls, my feet scrambling beneath me trying to find their strength, I knew that my life had changed. There was an indescribable stench of strangers hanging in the air, sweat mixed with drugs and the potent reek of urine. Precious items were dashed to the floor and lay like flotsam and jetsam on the shoreline after a violent storm. Upstairs my clothes spewed from their drawers like vomit from a seasick sailor and badly spelt graffiti adorned my bedroom walls. I stumbled back downstairs to the kitchen, where the churn of destruction looked like the aftermath of a flood. The impact of this violence made me reel and I choked on the fluids of adrenaline that were flowing in my throat. My harbour of safety had been violated and wrecked beyond repair. For the teenagers who had done this, it must have been a 'well good,' mobile phone, slap happy moment. But for me I wasn't waving at this point, I was drowning.

The Path to the River

Joanna Campbell

❧

The day he lost the last of his hair, my father fished in the river at the end of the garden. A secret path led to the bank. It began from our decrepit conservatory as an ordinary walk across the well-trodden grass. But then the lawn disappeared and became light-starved earth under racks of bracken. The trees leant forwards and pompously beckoned.

Adults always stopped at the end of the lawn and turned back to the more orderly patio or inspected the well-trained rose arbour. But children confronted the sticky ground with relish. To push through the branches, ducking the low boughs and disengaging hair or clothes from twigs, was to find another realm. Johnny used to say it was a different era. It was something else.

Bravery was required. That's why only children stooped and thrusted through, caking their shoes with mud and snagging their jerseys. Adults preferred to remain whole. I used to say it was because they couldn't see the sky any more. They couldn't have those tea-stirring conversations about 'looks like rain' or 'it's brightening up'. They couldn't avoid things by gazing at clouds.

Johnny and I developed a shell, I must admit. We didn't fancy nettle stings and thorn-whippings every time we disappeared. So we drove a nail into the frame of the conservatory door, which almost disintegrated, and hung oil-skin coats there. We shrugged them on as we left and slid our fishing rods underneath, along our spines, slotting them under the hanging-label in the collar. Then we pulled the hoods over our heads as we arched our stiffened backs and crawled into the secret path, two tortoises with slick skins. The noise was the best part. Crashing through bracken. Cracking sticks with our boots. Oilskins creaking. Our boots had soles as thick as sandwiches and were jagged to pinch in the wet soil and leave the suede on top unblemished.

Straightening up when we saw the water was Johnny's favourite part. He never said that because boys don't really chant their favourite things. But I knew. He would stand there and breathe. I knew he was filling up with the earthy damp air. He would wedge his heavy boots into the bank with his legs a full stride apart and his hands on his hips.

My father never fished with Johnny and me. He was an adult. When we came in late for tea, he looked with disdain at our filthy hands and refused to speak. My mother put a nail-brush by the soap in the cloakroom, but we only used it for scrubbing tackle when the mood took us.

We liked our grime. A mixture of mud, bits of bait and traces of Mars.

She would talk in a polite way and we would answer her kindly, glancing at my father for signs of softening. He would concentrate on his toasted sardines as if they were the most important fish he had ever seen. Taut conversation petered out. There was only the sound of persistent cutlery. I tried to keep my knife and fork quiet, even silent. But Johnny scraped his more than usual and swung his knife to collide often with the crystal cruets.

My father hated Johnny. No one ever said this, but it was plain. Johnny tested and probed, waiting for a reaction that never came. But my mother adored him. She always told the story of how she found a stiff dead shrew in his pocket and how he said that he'd had to keep it because it was still warm.

It was always Johnny who introduced new things to our fishing days. The first thing was Fishing Nights. Dark cold is painful, but neither one of us would admit defeat. The white moon-light on the black water pulled up the fish. The water was a cauldron groaning with life. It boiled with the smell of salmon. And once, a long prowling pike, baring its teeth on the grass while Johnny found a special net.

The next thing was Fishing with Mother. She was docile enough not to frighten the fish, but we knew she was longing to slip back to her pastry dough or her macramé. But she did it for Johnny. She wasn't willing to use the secret path and so we had to escort her out of the house and onto the road and then turn right and double back along the purplish track. Then we had to haul her up the slope and she stopped looking like my mother and more like a split tomato. Red, puffing cheeks and determined smile. Johnny made her touch the maggots. I hated seeing her finger in the squirming tin. And her squealing.

Then there was Fishing with Girls. Johnny was harsh and made them use the path. Maureen Hunter lost her glasses on the way and was in tears because her parents would kill her. Johnny tried to distract her with a cheese and salad-cream roll. She should have been more impressed because Johnny didn't usually have patience with crying. And it upset the fish. I felt girls were a mistake. They kept wiping their hands and knees with tissues and asking when we could go for a walk on the main road and catch the bus to the lido.

Then there was Fishing with Masturbation. But Johnny said we had to go our separate ways for that and then I felt there was too much of me. I couldn't relax, even with a spare coat spread over my lap and a good magazine. I preferred proper fishing with Johnny. I made him agree a time to meet up again and, when we did, I never knew whether to smile at him or not.

The path grew denser when Johnny left home. Our space vanished. I had school and homework. There was a Saturday job in a petrol station and rhythm guitar in a band. I had a girlfriend called Deborah. She was a limpet. I took up football and archery to avoid her, just saw her on Saturday nights. She was as cunning as an eel. At gigs she'd turn up with a quiche. The rest of the band fell on her pastry. If I was in a match, she'd be on the touchline, blowing on her hands. I told her sometimes I was fishing and no girls were allowed.

I didn't fish though and the path grew over.

Last Spring, I noticed my father wasn't going to work. I was revising for exams in my room one morning and he pelted his fists on my door.

"Turn that row off!"

The good thing about study leave was being with loud music. I resented my father for spoiling it. He tried to be helpful with bowls of soup for lunch and coffee every hour, but I wanted to be alone with crisps in my room. He set the table and called me in a companionable way, looking sort of humble but proud as we sat down. I was scared he might say Grace or make us use serviettes.

My mother had started a job, but he seemed to have finished his. He was awkward, as though he didn't actually belong here. He didn't understand home. My mother would have let me read at the table if just she and I were there. But he wanted to talk. He thought I would like to talk about school or Deborah. I just withered him with a look and put a foot up on the empty chair next to me. He was spiking up his hair with agitated fingers and I glanced up. His spoon was drowning in his tomato soup. His slice of bread was torn in half and one half looked like a rectangle with a dent and the other rectangle had a bump to fit the dent.

"I have left work. I am having cancer treatment at the hospital. It makes me very tired and sick."

He was like a talking Janet and John book. All concise sentences. I looked down at my empty bowl, imagining him running his index finger under each word.

"It's in my lung. Only the one."

There was a kind of rhyme there.

I couldn't picture him in a long gown at the hospital. I only knew him in a suit and tie. Except today was a Monday and he was wearing loose fawn trousers with the belt not threaded through each loop. It was wrong.

"I have a chance. It might go away. We have to be patient."

He used his teacher's voice. He might as well have been facing his fourth form. "Settle down, 5C, please. Turn to page 65. The heart of a fish has two chambers. A human heart has four. This is because a fish heart pumps blood in only one direction."

"OK." That was all I could say.

He fitted his bread halves together and passed me the plate.

He put on pink rubber gloves to wash up and I kicked the chair away and left the house. I thought 'OK' was enough. Males didn't make fusses. OK was OK.

It was cooling for my eyes out in the wild afternoon. The wind bit my face. I pulled on my oil-skin and made for the path, blundering through the thick growth and breathing in the old leaves and spores. Spring was slow to produce sap in here. I had my eyes half closed and pushed my way into the deepest part. Johnny called it The Reaching. Branches implored you deeper in, pressed against you, then yielded to your weight and closed behind you. My boots knew the path. They knew each jumble of dead roots. I didn't need to see. I could smell the river. It was like opening a can of ginger beer or sniffing pear drops if you haven't had them for years. Takes you back. Fits you into an old space.

It was slimy on the bank in our best spot and there was a decaying tree nearby that grated in the wind. I was sore with cold and wishing that I wasn't concealed from the house. I wanted my father to see me from an upstairs window and come crunching through the path, the rushing sound of him coming closer and closer, hurrying to me and sweeping me up into his big arms so I could inhale tobacco and mint and Imperial Leather and press my face against his jumper.

I hurled stones into the ruffled water, harder and harder, wishing and waiting. Then rain pelted down and it felt like acid in the wind. I struggled back and found the lawn was dry and my father was hanging up the washing with pegs in his mouth. I went up to him.

"The Australian lungfish only has one lung. It uses it when the river runs dry."

My father stared with his mouth open.

"And it sounds like a little pair of bellows."

I went inside and listened to the drone of the dishwasher. My mother usually turned machines on at night and shut the door on them. Deborah was ringing the door bell. I knew her ring. It was lots of staccato pings with regular gaps. She was wearing a difficult-looking dress with folds and pleats and a fiddly tie-belt. Her eye-shadow was a yellow sherbet colour to match the dress. She was sparkling at me like a determined wedge of lemon.

"Surprise! Is anyone home? Shall we go upstairs?" Her cod-eyes flashed at me. She could hear my father. He was beating eggs in the kitchen now. She raised her eyebrows in confusion.

"My old man's at home today. Day off kind of thing. We're going fishing in a minute." I didn't ask her in, even though the wind was beating at her dress and stiffening the hairs on her arms.

"Oh." She never stayed defeated though. "Tell you what, if you've got an old pair of jeans and a jumper, I could go with you. You could come upstairs with me and find something."

She was angling for an afternoon of fishing with sex. Johnny and I had never done that. The girls we took to the river were just for kissing. And we soon tired of that. I nearly bit Jane Vangelly's lip off when I got a bite from a giant carp.

I thought of frantic held-breath-writhing on my quilt with my father whisking eggs in the room below and felt sick. Deborah was grinning with her long front teeth resting on her bottom lip and her brows up under her fringe.

Then my father wandered into the hall with his glass bowl and beater.

"Hello, Deborah. Just making some batter."

"Very organised, Mr Bateman. All ready to coat the fish. Are we having chips as well?"

"It's Pancake Day. Needs to stand for a while, so I'm told. So Delia says. I'll just go and wait while it rests."

His wrist worked efficiently. The beater swirled the eggs up into long waves tipped with froth. The sound of splashing and chinking metal on glass made me think of my mother and Johnny and round after round of pancakes. My father was still wearing the rubber gloves and whistling.

I did the same when I was fishing, waiting for a bite in the drizzle for hours. I whistled between my teeth in a sort of hiss until Johnny glared and threw a hook at me.

Deborah was waiting for me to choose between the river and sex. She would snap up either option or both together if my father wasn't coming. Her head was tilted, her eyes unblinking, fixed on my face. Glancing at the kitchen doorway, I could see my father massaging the frying pan with oil and then halving lemons. Citrus fumes wafted into the hall as the juice pooled on the chopping board.

"I've got a miniature brandy in my bag," Deborah said, as if tempting a child with a bag of jelly beans.

My father was spearing the half-lemons onto the squeezer, cupping his hands over them, twisting them firmly back and forth.

"So what are we doing?"

Her voice was sharp. I could never take her to the river. I looked up. Johnny was on the lawn, strutting in his familiar way, shoulders bobbing from side to side, legs wide apart, trousers flapping like pennants in the wind. "Fancy a walk later? Who's your friend? Just saying goodbye are you?"

He looked at her with indifference. She melted away like a pat of butter in the sun. I saw the hedge was filled with damp butterflies and the cat was pouncing on a spider by the milk bottles my father had rinsed and left out for the morning. I saw the clouds sliding apart and the starlings regroup to begin their afternoon sky dance.

Johnny clattered into the hall and I waited there at the door, looking at a bush of cream roses, tinged brown at the edges, soaking the air with scent. It was the silence that made me look at the kitchen. My father and Johnny were locked together, speechless with tears.

Johnny and I went down to the river later and I wanted to ask why they hugged, but Johnny's mood was rancid and the fish we caught were useless. We tossed them back into the river, dark as blood in the still evening. Johnny was staring at me as I flung the last one.

"Why didn't you say anything? Dad said you mumbled 'OK' and went out. Then some stuff about Australia and bellows"

"He was talking oddly and it felt all wrong."

"Well, wouldn't you? If you were dying?"

Johnny was standing, his long shadow staining the moss, livid green in the last light.

"I was a bit shocked. You weren't there. You don't know how it was."

"He told me."

"Why are you so bothered anyway? He doesn't even like you." I hated the words being out. They hung there in the fading day, the starlings wheeling above to announce the night. I could just hear Johnny's shallow breathing. He was packing his tackle and closing tins of bait. He spoke at last.

"I never asked him to like me. I'm Mum's, not his. He took us both on."

Johnny went without waiting for me. I stayed for a long time. Johnny was with the adults. I wondered if they would leave me any pancakes.

The growing summer brought the river to life while my father shrank. He sat on a deck-chair by the roses like a little old man, wheeled outside for the sun to exhaust him. Shiny head slumping, jaw slack. My mother and Johnny quietly ran the house while I watched him from my window.

Johnny whistled the day he took my father fishing and supported him out of the house and onto the road and then they turned right and doubled back along the purplish track. Then it was up the slope to just the right spot. I could follow the start of their progress from my window, even though they eventually dipped out of sight.

Don't Tell Me the Story

Brindley Hallam Dennis

CƷ

Martin sat in the café with a half full cafetiere of coffee in front of him, making it last. He knew they wouldn't mind, because the place was more than half empty. He was sitting in one of the window seats, where he could be seen from the street.

It was to see the street that Martin had sat there. He was watching the people. It amazed him to see them walk. How many ways there were of doing it, this simple thing that he had learned before the age of two?

Some walked as if the paved square were a field of mud, pressing their heavy feet firmly down. Some walked as if on a deck, rolling slightly in an unseen swell. Some walked with delicacy, as if something carried above must not be spilled. Some walked with a wobble. Some walked with several wobbles. Some strode. Some scurried. Some advanced, heads turned away, as if they were blind. Some were blind. Some walked as if to avoid being seen. Some walked as if only to be seen.

For each walk, more so than for each person, Martin could imagine a frame of mind: resignation; determination; exultation; relaxation. He could devise stories for each walk: where it came from; where it was going.

The walks were stories in themselves, untold stories: stories you had to make up for yourself, from what you saw. Having said that, for all his imagination, they were false stories, and he knew that for each imagining there would be countless other possibilities, only one of which, at best, might be the true.

The counter staff watched him watching, each one imagining who it was that he was waiting for, and why.

Beware the Carousel

Matthew B Dexter

ߕ

Girls in The Gravitron are slutty. At least that's the rumor in my town. Most fathers think The Gravitron is the dangerous ride. They don't know the Ferris Wheel is the mother of all murderers. Dad never lets me ride The Gravitron, says the centrifugal force is three times that of gravity. The inertia of my madness moves a little slower. Dad's always holding me back.

"Not until you're taller."

"That kid only hit his head because he was doing it wrong."

"Accidents happen."

Every afternoon around dusk Mom picks me up and Dad disappears, says he's going to have a drink with his buddies. But today I tell Mom we're going over to a friend's house, follow Dad as he criss-crosses between cotton candy machines, face painting booths, animal balloons, ticket stands, chilli corndogs, and the ever-present effervescent chunks of fluorescent heroin used to lure over-sugared children.

Dad walks fast, sweeping in and out of traffic like a puppy looking for his master. He ends up in the corner of the carnival by the trees, trash cans, bees, and mothers hovering over little boys who ate too much garbage. Dad floats toward the beer booth and buys a couple Coors. He drinks them standing. Where are his friends? The foam collects on his lips beneath the sinking sun. He buys two more. Yellow jackets circle his plastic cups. He doesn't mind. Nothing fazes him. He no longer looks like my dad; he's morphed into a different mindset, a secret life.

Hiding behind a maple tree soaked in vomit, I watch it all: Dad's eyes attached to the rides, the women, the screams, and the putrid smell of sickness drifting through humid air. He sips beer and watches the Ferris wheel, Funhouse, the Whip. Kiddie rides don't interest him. He hands cash to a homeless man digging through Styrofoam trash – redeeming himself as my hero – until the donation is wasted on four more beers. They sit Indian style in the grass and drink like hobos. Dad's talking loud, laughing with this madman Mom would never give the time of day. The vagrant's words make no sense to me, but Dad seems to understand.

"Wanna ride The Gravitron?"

The man's mouth opens; mostly toothless. Eyes like roman candles, pupils expand as fireflies come into focus, approach us from the magical place these fairies hide during the day. The whole affair makes me want to throw up a little in my mouth, want to kick Dad in the shins and see what he says, but I need to dig deeper into the decrepit carnie hole he crawls into when me and Mom go grocery shopping. He's in a different world as I stare for fifteen minutes into the lobster tank.

They finish their beers. Dad orders two more.

"Rocket fuel."

They wander off toward the crowd, lost in the iridescent insanity. Following them toward The Gravitron, people stop and stare at the disheveled homeless man holding my father's hand. So this is what he does when he gets drunk? Dad dances to the rhythm of Metallica as they hand over their tickets, wait in line. Kids are laughing, but Dad doesn't give a damn. He's going to ride the lighting. Most of these tools weren't even born when metal was at its best. Neither was I.

Only thing keeping tears from streaming down my cheeks is the third grader waiting in line a couple dozen people behind Dad. The machine is going crazy. We can hear the screaming. Beams of light making love on our faces, it feels like an awakening as the orange moon watches unaware.

Time expires; teenagers waddle away from the mechanism. A couple punks puke in the grass behind the majestic open-mouthed contraption. It swallows Dad. The chick sees me, asks, "Ya wanna ride it with me?"

"I'm too young." Don't want to admit I'm too short. She's at least a foot taller, boobs pondering their existence.

"My cousin works here." She points to the gothic monster taking tickets, standing at the entrance to the gates of heaven. I look at the vomit and bubble gum on my shoes. There's a chunk of caramel popcorn in her hair. She's making love to her box of Cracker Jacks.

"I would, but my dad's on this thing, he can't see me."

Butterflies and dragonflies have sex in my stomach as she giggles.

"Put this on."

It's a ghost mask. Almost wet my pants. Dreaming of reaching second base, she places it over my face and hands her tickets to the lunatic of her uncle's loins.

"Have fun Casper."

The machine smells even stronger than I imagined: fresh vomit, cotton candy, dirty socks, and something extra. The girls in The Gravitron are pulling down their shirts, tucking them into their shorts, not slutty behavior by any standards. It disappoints me. Maybe they wait till they start the revolutions? Dad and the wino are already spinning, rubbing arms, laughing like the worst town drunks on an awful binge.

The door closes and the man returns to the middle: where the magic happens. Dad is hysterical as the centrifugal force pulls us backwards, sideways we spin, spiders in paradise. Dad signals to the captain. The microphone comes to life and warns not to walk on walls or get upside-down. Dad struggles onto his knees as we pick up speed. The captain is snorting into the microphone, rubbing the tip of his nose. The homeless man is urinating himself. My mask falls off as Dad rises to his feet and begins walking around on the walls. I've never been prouder in my life.

He smiles as a child tries to kick him in the nuts. Only the strong can maintain themselves when The Gravitron really gets kicking. Metallica is still raging. *Master of Puppets* is pulling the strings to my father's madness, making him dance and people are shouting. Dad smacks his head against a metal bar.

"Look at this fool."

"Sometimes he does this naked."

The machine nearing maximum velocity, his blood looks like vomit and we chase it in circles, this comet of our inertia. Never felt closer to my father than that evening in The Gravitron, leaning on third grade breasts, the stars so bright and big.

Over the Top

Max Dunbar

છ

In his dream he was on the wrong train and ended up in a part of the city he'd never been before, ran into Dee Halstone who was with Trent Ferdinand and a few other guys and after a coupla beers in a coupla pubs they were running through the streets, music booming from somewhere, the chant rose up from Trent in his wheelchair: THIS IS ROCK AND ROLL! THIS IS ROCK AND ROLL! – and clattering down a set of stairs into the hole of a tunnel with an unfazed working man stood by the closed doors saying "Sorry, lads, it's six am," which gave him a jolt of anxiety, seeing as the company were on manoeuvres at nine, but fuck it, do the whole day through –

- *whoosh.* The delta waves echoed away into his head. No worry about work after all. All gone in a few hours, but he still had enough memory to understand that he and Dee (Dee and I) had met several times that week, juddering towards each other on grass and precinct, and he wondered whether the dream world kept going when you were awake, some kind of parallel life where the rules were different.

Corvair was standing by the kettle. "A brew, Lance-Corporal?"

"Wouldn't mind, sir."

A crash shook the room. He sidestepped a little but kept his balance; Corvair himself didn't react. The men in the bunks barely stirred; you wouldn't expect them to. Lossario had always said that the soldier's greatest talent is to sleep on command. And speak of the devil –

Corvair handed him his brew in the MCFC mug. The captain offered a cigarette, waited till it was lit before he spoke. "I've heard from the man. We move at some point within the next four hours."

"Good stuff. Climbing up the fucking walls here!"

Typical squaddie gallows humour, you might have said – and yet there was truth in it. It would be good to get out of this bulletproof box where they'd been since the debacle at Heliom, nothing to do but chat and read and work their way through the spoils of looting. Even though the alternative was almost certain death at the Faith's guns. Would everyone feel this way, that oblivion is better than boredom and stasis?

"Good timin, I suppose. I see you're running out of book, there."

Schiazzi's old man had given him Shelby Foote's entire Civil War opus. Schiazzi had no interest in reading, and had told his father so, but the old man had just shook his head and said: *You never know when you're gonner get bored, son.* Dad had been right, as he generally was. The past month he'd been racing through the Foote omnibus, cannibalising the read pages for kindling and bog roll.

The others stirred awake. Schiazzi knew that there would be no momentary *where-am-I* shit, not for his kind. Breakfasts of Pot Noodles and Rustlers ready meals were made from kettle and microwave. More brews, cigarettes rolled and lit, and Corvair slapped open the chessboard crying winner stays on, as he always did. He shared his news, which was received in a deep and abiding indifference. The guns rolled as if to underline the point.

"Well, if that's the case," said Edlington, "might as well break out the moonshine now."

"We start drinking your latest batch," Corvair said, "there'll be no need to go over the top. Man, at least the Faith guns are *quick*."

Atkinson: "In any case, what happens if the big lads get here, and we're all like: Tally-ho, old England! Rarr, ya fuck-fugh-fugh..." He mimed a sloppy, drunken salute that made Schiazzi think of *Red Dwarf*.

"Come on, no one's gonner care about that now. Anyway, beer improves fucking performance. When I won the Blackwater Cross at Torry Astell..." The rest of this was submerged in mocking groans: they had heard the story many times.

"Mention that one more time, soldier, I'll put that medal in a place where you'll always be reminded of its significance," Corvair told him. "But you're right. Might as well start drinking early."

Edlington's amateur moonshine was brewed over three-day periods, using Alliance-brand sachet sugar, a bushel of wheat they had found in a bombed-out farmhouse in Trestle, and medicinal ethanol; and tested pretty much how you'd expect. On this day, however, it did its job. Corvair beat them a few go-rounds on the board and Schiazzi read about Pickett's charge, but within a couple of hours they were all bouncing off each other's ideas and lying back laughing, and Schiazzi now changed his mind, that he didn't want to leave, they were having a good laugh, and the wonder and absurdity of their situation (from that to *this*?) didn't detract from the atmosphere. The guns rolled again at that point, making Schiazzi think as always of the crunch of boot on Cheshire gravel, the sound their Volvo made as it turned into his grandfather's driveway.

They were singing 'David Lossario's Men' now, which Schiazzi hadn't heard since it had been pounded into him at process centre. The company got into its second verse before memory failed and they were rocking back on their pallets again with laughter, toasting each other with mugs and water-cooler cups.

Atkinson stood up – just about. The others cheered at his compromised gait. He said: "Christ, this is bad." He pulled out a bag of Wine Gums from under his bunk.

"Fuck's this?" Schiazzi laughed.

"Saving 'em for a special occasion." He opened the bag and started chucking them out.

"Most soldiers keep *paw-now*-graphy under their beds!"

"Hey, we're gonner be ripping the veils off peasant girls this time tomorrow," Schiazzi said.

Corvair spat out a mess of red gelatin. "Man," he declared, "that Wine Gum was more trouble than it was worth!"

Schiazzi wondered if it was all over soon whether the parallel track of his dreams would keep on going. Would these adventures be derailed by the bullets tearing into his prefrontal cortex? Outside the guns rolled and then stopped and then rolled again.

We Have Come a Long Way From Where We Are

Dorothy Fryd

ൠ

In Ffestiniog railway station waiting room, a man sits with his head in his hands. He is not wearing shoes. When Grace enters the waiting room, she looks at the man and wonders what has happened to him to make his hands tremble.

A train slowly passes them and the flashing light rouses the man and he raises his head. The train passengers look at the two strangers in the waiting room and feel glad to be inside an air conditioned carriage. Grace looks into the man's eyes and watches his pupils slowly dilate. The man looks at Grace.

Grace knows that the man wants to talk. As Grace turns her shoulder to leave the room, the man speaks to her, saying something which she can't quite determine.

Grace thinks about her father. He told her that a person can recall anything they hear within twenty seconds. She wonders if her father will now be entirely bald. She thinks about what she will do when she reaches him.

-I said, I found my wife in bed with another man.

Grace turns to face the man, giving him her full attention.

-Do you have any idea? He continues, unable to meet Grace's eyes. *Two hours ago, I held a gun to my wife's head and nearly pulled the trigger.*

Grace fingers the gun in her own pocket.

The man draws a figure of eight with his big toe. Grace looks at the figure of eight. She is hypnotised. She replays the image of the big toe and the figure of eight for thirty seconds. She is about to use her voice for the first time in six years. She clears her throat. She wonders if her voice will work.

-I'm sorry she says, her voice cracking and juddering and starting up.

Garage Apartment

Wayne Lee Gay

 co

There's something about a garage apartment, three blocks away from a college campus, that makes people decide to leave evidence of a special favorite vice behind when they move out, and not care anymore if the landlady finds out, once they're gone.

Mother inherited our rambling old house – and the garage, and the apartment above the garage – from her father. With the insurance settlement after my father died, she was able not to work, but just barely. We were always scrabbling a little bit, always wishing we had more, always sure we needed to rent out the garage apartment to make ends meet. We'd only see inside the apartment between renters, which never happened for long, thanks to the eminently rentable location. But whenever someone moved out, Mother would react in horror, shock, and disdain at whatever it was the renter had left behind.

"Who would have thought?" she would say, shaking her head in despair. "All that time, right here *literally* in our own back yard." And then, with a finality that said she had put it behind her, "Thank God, that one's gone."

As my brother and sister and I got older, we came to realize she said the same thing every time someone moved away. There was always something left behind, like the stacks of little green pornographic novellas that the assistant basketball coach at the university left. Neat stacks of exactly fifty. My brother Rick managed to filch half a dozen and hide them under his mattress.

Then, there was the bin full of empty scotch bottles left by Miss Hopkins, a small, neat woman, administrative assistant to the dean of the college of arts and sciences. She left one hundred and four bottles, which meant she was knocking back two whole bottles a week.

"Could be worse," my sister Louise said.

Mother narrowed her eyes and looked at Louise suspiciously.

Mother was even more suspicious when Frank, a nice young law student, took the apartment, but she had no excuse *not* to rent it to him. He biked the three blocks to campus and kept very odd hours. Some nights, he didn't even come home at all.

"Probably studying," Louise said, one morning when, from the breakfast table, we all saw him bike home and climb up the fragile little stairway that led up to his door.

A few days later, Louise came in the back door at dinner time.

"I don't want you going over there any more," Mother said.

"Mother, we were just talking." Louise was seventeen, and beautiful, with long red hair that she pulled back with a confident, tossing motion as she sat down.

"Besides, he's a law student, he knows all about age of consent laws," Rick threw in, just to make matters worse.

"Am I under age?" Louise asked.

"Stop that this minute," Mother said. "Under age doesn't matter because *nothing is going to be going on!*"

I was fifteen and fascinated.

Frank moved out the next summer.

"Wonder what it'll be this time?" Rick muttered as we watched Mother her carry the broom and mop and empty garbage bags up the rickety wooden stair that lead to the apartment's only entrance. "Porn? Booze? He looked more like a pothead to me."

"Mmmm, I'd guess serial killer," Louise said. "The back closet is probably full of dead bodies. Or bones."

Three hours later, Mother was back. I sat at the kitchen table, scribbling at my homework. Louise was on her way out to a movie with friends and Rick had just hung up the phone.

"What a nice young man he was," Mother said. "For once, nothing shocking to clean up."

"I told you," Rick said. "He's a law student, and he's smart enough not to mess with under age girls."

"I'm not under age," Louise said, gathering her red hair into a pony tail. "Alice and I looked it up. Seventeen is legal in this state."

"Well, it doesn't matter," Mother said, "Since you're not going to be doing anything anyway, until you get married. *Literally.*"

"Smart guy, that Frank," Rick said. "Probably going to be governor some day. Or a famous trial lawyer. Like Perry Mason."

I stared at my algebra homework, and didn't say anything. And knew that Frank wasn't smart enough not to mess around with an under age boy. But he was smart enough not to let anyone know.

And so was I.

Probably.

Issues

Alan Gillespie

Ꮨ

Benny calls out whether someone's walking past or not. "Bigishoooo! Err yer bigishoo." He stands nestled beneath a sandstone archway, and winks at me, his magazines held out like a dowsing rod. "Ta very much, Godblessye hen." "Much obliged sur, huvagoodday."

His clothes are shabby but clean, frayed cuffs and wet shoes. Four magazines sell between 8am and 10am, earning him six pounds and eighty pence. The street falls quiet after the morning rush of office and shop workers. You're not supposed to move around, he tells me, but you have to keep moving. There's another patch near the train station that should get some traffic.

I'm shadowing Benny for the day. Tomorrow it'll be just me, with my own bundle of magazines and a laminated tag around my neck. He's showing me the ropes by which I'll be tied. You need to be careful, he tells me. Can't trespass on someone else's territory. Can't stand on another man's toes. He's not specific about consequences.

The magazines are a precious commodity, Benny says. They're a form of currency. Take care nobody pinches them. And if someone's got something you want, swap them for it. He winks again.

"Bigishoooo! Err yer bigishoo." Benny bows and scrapes when someone pushes a cold coin into his palm. "Yass," he says, counting the metal discs. "Atz enuff furra bed the night."

One of the hotels will take him for a few pounds. I've got something sorted as well, free temporary accommodation at Hope House. They don't let you stay long. I'm supposed to get my name on a housing list. It's good for their statistics, apparently. A single bed for a single night, and then I'll be out on my own.

That night, stuck in limbo between sleep and nausea, I wrap my legs around the sheets and imagine I'm far away, with Harold again.

Harold always had the best taste in beds. It was impeccable.

23

I close my eyes and we're chug chug chugging, aboard the Orient Express, wrapped up in embroidered quilts that scratch my skin. Or we're spread out in a four poster at the Ritz, giggling like schoolchildren, eating purple cherries with dollops of yoghurt. Or we're sinking into waterbeds and gripping wrought-iron frames, and roll, roll, rolling through the night on an Arctic cruise. Harold was wonderful. He told me bed was like a stage. I always thought it was more like a canvas.

Not that we spent all our time together on a mattress. There were black tie evenings in art galleries, VIP rooms in cocktail bars, rooftop terraces sipping Hendrick's and tonic with cubes of cucumber, driving his Porsche in Italian shoes, splattering each other with paint in my studio, cufflink shopping at Tiffany's, first class flights, my penthouse apartment, walk-in wardrobe, balcony overlooking the river. Harold always left the rent money for me in an envelope on the dressing table.

I fall asleep on a stiff board in Hope House, wishing that he was still alive.

"Big Issue! Who wants a Big Issue?"

I don't have Benny's talent for salesmanship yet. He comes along to say hello, on his way to a promising patch outside the new shopping centre. He tells me to relax. Tells me I'll get used to the life after a day or two. Tells me to stay away from the shopping centre or he'll do me.

No wink.

I become invisible. Men walk past, smelling divine, ignoring me completely. Mothers push prams, facing straight ahead while their children stare. I sell one magazine, to a pensioner. She drops two grubby coins into my hand and I pat my pockets, even though I know I don't have change. Not to worry, she says. Just you keep it, son. I thank her very much and resist the urge to throw up. The way she looks at me, the way she looks through me, makes me loathe myself.

"Bigishoooo! Get your bigishoo."

I'm getting the hang of this. At least I think so. Two more copies sell. Nobody takes their change, but I should get some from the supermarket, just in case. Although that means I'll have to buy something.

When Harold died, I had some money to keep me going. When it began running out, I would shop at night, buying all the produce that was going off, at a reduced price. And when I could no longer afford that, I went round the back, through the bins. Peeling open stale sandwiches. Relieved and revolted.

I haven't really lived since Harold died. We were together for years. He knew every fancy and fetish and I was never disappointed. He spoiled me, of course he did. Because I loved him and he loved me. But when he died, all the wealth and comfort and security went to his wife. I wasn't welcome at the funeral. I wasn't mentioned in the will. I didn't get a penny. Friends, who'd known all about us, feigned ignorance and sidled up to her. Wiped her tears, held her hand, accepted her invitations to supper. If she ever knew about her husband's secret boyfriend she never let on. Harold never mentioned it, but I'm sure she knew. She must have.

When I was evicted from my flat, three months in arrears with the rent, it had been transformed. All the clean lines were gone. The minimalist, Swedish decor had been covered up. Blame it on artistic temperament.

I consider it my masterpiece. My homage to Harold. Onto every surface of the home he'd kept me in went layer upon layer of thick oil paint, swabbed on in dank tan and cold slate and sooty bistre, a whirlpool of everything I couldn't say. Onto the wooden floorboards I painted a swirling, turbulent vortex. The ceiling became a stratus of foggy cloud, like bottled exhaust fumes. I made the bath sheer black. Likewise the toilet.

I did the windows last: plum and cobalt, crimson and carrot, in thin brushstrokes portraying broken glass and dead sunflowers. Stroke by stroke the daylight faded, replaced by gloom, backlit like stained glass.

If this seems dramatic, well, I'm a painter. Always have been. A writer might have tortured himself with obscure verses. A musician might have sung ballads with tears in his eyes. It was just my way of mourning. Of trying to mourn.

"Bigishoooo! Get yer bigishoo."

It's raining and I've ended up in a rotten spot with no shelter. I'm scared to move because I've been warned, by a chin-scarred thug, that if he sees me near his plot again he'll have me. He's claimed the stairs outside the Church of Scotland for his own, been there seven years, find your own bloody patch. His clothes are new and his cheeks are plump. A middle-class tramp, of all things. I bet they bring him tea and polythene bags full of old stuff every Sunday.

My feet are sodden, breached by the rain, and my magazines wrinkle up. I wrap them in cellophane but it's useless. The drizzle's getting everywhere.

A policeman stops to check my ID. He's clean shaven, clothes neatly pressed. Big black shoes jutting out from flawless trousers. I want to cling onto his arm and bury my face in his chest. Want him to hold me. Someone tried to sell me drugs last night, I tell him. He's not interested. Maybe if I steal his hat he'll arrest me, take me in the back of his van, throw me in a cell for the night. But he's marching away, long legs, square shoulders.

The people walking past stare from beneath umbrellas. Eyes shifting over me. They're wondering how someone manages to ruin their life so much they end up like this. Wondering what I did to deserve it. Wondering where I'll sleep tonight.

I wonder too.

It's my own fault. That's the worst thing. This was avoidable. I just wasn't looking where I was going. After I graduated from art school I sold a few paintings. My debts were deep but a list of contacts kept me ticking over for a while. I made money from time to time. When I sold a piece I spoiled myself until the funds ran out, spending months in Paris, in Athens, in Venice. I got by on youth and enthusiasm and bursaries and the contents of other men's pockets. And then I met Harold. It was all different with him. I told him I was his and that I wasn't going anywhere. He told me he was mine and that he would give me anything. And then Harold died.

It's been years since I painted anything worth more than the cost of the materials. I've no pension. No income. No assets. My buttocks have sunk down low and my arms have deflated. I used to be a package, a catch, a trophy boyfriend. I never thought the day would come when I couldn't cling onto the coattails of a repressed homosexual with money.

You'd be amazed how many men are married with children, driving the Land Rover, holidaying in Mallorca, celebrating anniversaries, double dating, dinner partying, sleeping in queen sized marital beds, all the time denying their instinct. And it's because gay relationships just aren't the same. It's cruel but they don't have that gravitas; not in the real world, where prejudice and phobias are much more commonplace than the BBC lets you believe. In a gay relationship you rely on each other as best friends as well as partners. You've got yourself a friend/lover/partner hybrid. And when he's gone, you're isolated. Alone. Condemned.

The magazines aren't shifting and my nose starts to drip. I pack it in and go to the underground station. For the price of a single journey I can stay down there for hours, ten feet under, going round and round the wet city in circles.

I flick through one of my magazines on the train, trying to blend in. Trying to look like a normal man who's just bought one, rather than an outsider trying to hawk them off. One page catches my eye. It's the kind of article I once would've read from back to front.

Says there's a Van Gogh exhibit opening at the Kelvingrove museum. *The Starry Night*'s going up for all of Glasgow to see. Says it's worth a hundred million dollars. That much for one painting. It baffles me. Makes me question all those years when I stuck my nose up in the air and ooh-ed and aah-ed at things hanging from walls.

The train stops at a station. It's late afternoon and people are going home, thousands of clockwork mice following their routine. A girl sits next to me, long legs crossed, a defensive pose. I glance at her perfect skin, can't stop looking. I'm making her uncomfortable.

Soon it'll be dark and I'll be alone in the streets. I think that maybe I'll go along to the Van Gogh exhibition this weekend. Maybe I'll run into one of the old crowd. One of Harold's business associates. A friendly face. They might want to take me for a coffee. Maybe lunch. Who knows where it could lead?

The girl gets off at her stop. I wonder who's waiting for her on the other side of the barriers. The pleats of her skirt brush my hand.

I've ended up right on the lip of society. I'm clinging on with fingertips but I've seen people who've been chewed up and spat out the system altogether. No passport, no P60, no state pension. Nameless people that can't even get an NHS doctor. Some receptionist saying "What's yer name?" and "What's yer address?" and that's that.

Can't get a house if you've no job. Can't get a job if you've no address.

Best place to end up is jail. You're still outwith society, removed from the civilised structure, but at least you get a roof. At least you're not a nothing.

When I leave the underground station it's night. In a supermarket I buy Grant's gin and value tonic water. No food. I walk over the Clyde, on a footbridge, swigging from both bottles one after the other. It slips down my throat like heartburn.

Shuffling footsteps to my left and Benny appears, of all people, crazy-eyed and unsteady. "Magine findin yoo here," he says. "Howzitgaun? A wee drink wid be magic, ta."

I never noticed before, but he's toothless. Pink gums between dark chops. He looks at me, scuffs his feet. Sips from the bottle and looks up and down the road. No traffic. Sips again. Kicks me in the gut and rips the scarf from my neck, twisting me to the ground. Then he's running away, scarf flapping loose and gin slopping from the bottle, over his knuckles, into the gutter.

I hold onto the railing and pull myself up. Below, the water is inky, churning currents and frothy spit, reflected streetlights dancing in the dark. I lean over the edge, see my breath catching and crystallising in the cold air. I close my eyes. Harold, I whisper. Harold, for God's sake.

The Starry Night's twenty nine inches by thirty six. Big. But not too big. I know every corner of the Kelvingrove, every doorway and crevice. Used to go there all the time. Exhibitions, opening nights, fundraisers. Even a few weddings – me and Harold sitting side by side in the pews, hands folded across our laps, ankles intertwined.

Prison's not a place someone normally desires to be. And there's people would rather live in a bin than behind bars, but that's them, not me. I'm not used to this. I hate the cold. I miss walls and roofs. I miss interaction. If it's a question of survival, sheer survival, some people can handle living on the streets but I can't. I need the system. I need society, even if it's one running behind prison walls.

Getting in the door's the hard part, I reckon. Once you're inside it you can kick up a fuss, cause some trouble and make sure you're not released. But how to get there in the first place? I can't murder. I couldn't handle being in a wing surrounded by killers. Besides, it seems unnecessary.

Theft it is then. And what better to steal than the medium I've spent my life pretending to appreciate, pretending to create? A thousand and forty four square inches of canvas and oil. A hundred million dollars. Dutch fingerprints melted into the sky. That's the curious thing about paint: you use it wet, have a slim window of time to mould and spread it just the way you like and then it sets, and it's solid, for the rest of your days and many more besides.

You need to get things in order when you've got the chance, because if you leave it too long the game's a bogey.

So I'll steal the painting, get caught, and go to jail. Or steal the painting, get away with it, and sell it. I can't really see a downside to either option.

I pick a cigarette butt out the bin and light up. Feel the smoke curling down my throat. Wander up and down the path alongside the museum. It's closing time. The lights inside flicker and fade. The staff leave. Someone's left a window open.

The sky's dark blue and the lights from the city drown out the stars, swirling about in a yellow-orange haze. The university tower's bold against the backdrop, reaching up and out with boughs of brick. Rain falls, oily and black.

"Bigishoooo! Err yer bigishoo." But there's nobody around. And even if there was, I'm invisible, remember? I merge into the shadows and slip inside.

Lovers of the Planet

Louise Halvardsson

୧୫

I just need one more lover. One more person to join me and thousands of other lovers all over the planet. One more and I can keep my job.

It's dark and the streets are busy with the 9-to-5 lot making their way home. There's a smell of rain in the air, mingling with the car fumes. I wouldn't like to be stuck in an office or a shop all day, but sometimes I don't get home until the late news starts.

I need to recruit at least three lovers a day. It doesn't sound like a lot, considering that I call at hundreds of doors but most people peer through the curtains when they hear the bell and retreat to the back of their houses when they spot my green uniform and heart-shaped badge, refusing to open the door, even if I press the bell long and hard enough to give them tinnitus.

The house I'm outside now is part of a semi-detached row that could do with some decorating. This one is in a particularly bad state, blue paint peeling from the door. There's no bell. I knock until my knuckles hurt. The curtains twitch and a couple of seconds later the door opens. A whiff of something stale, like unwashed sheets and cigarette smoke, comes towards me.

"What do you want?" A girl, a few years older than me, perhaps in her late twenties, is holding on to the door handle. She's got the look I'd spent hours failing to recreate: the *I-just-got-out-of bed*-look. Red hair in a perfect mess, baggy T-shirt with *Lucky Strike* logo, nipples poking out like cigarette butts and faded jeans with big holes in the knees. Natural holes. Before I got this job I used a pair of scissors to fix my Levi's, and deliberately spilt paint on them to make myself look like a slacker.

It had failed. The woman at the job centre said I was fully capable of doing a day's work.

"What do you want?" the girl asks again. I'm amazed that she hasn't shut the door in my face. I smile. It's part of the training: look friendly. I spent a morning practising smiles in front of the mirror before embarking on my first round of door-knocking. The smile I'm giving the red-haired girl is wide as a rainbow.

"Have you heard about Lovers of the Planet? We're a new charity and it's our job to find more lovers."

The girl runs her fingers through her hair. They get stuck in a tangle above an ear pierced with a metal stud. She looks the type, who, in the right mood, would care enough for the planet to give it some money.

"So what do you do?" she asks, fingering the metal stud. "Rub yourself with soil and fuck rabbits?"

I ignore the teasing twinkle in her voice and step closer. She doesn't move or leave any space for me to enter her house. It's a shame because once I'm inside people will sign anything just to get rid of me. My climate change rant lasts about five minutes but my throat is dry and it sounds like I've got a cold.

"We're trying to persuade the government to subsidise supermarkets who buy local produce. You and I can make a difference because…"

"Because what?" The girl leans forward, leaving only an inch between our lips. To my surprise her breath smells of toothpaste. Spit flies out of her mouth and lands on my chin as she speaks. "This planet is already fucked. It doesn't matter where my veggies come from. If I buy them from the farmer down the road some farmer in Kenya will suffer because he can't export his green beans…"

"That's not the point!" I step back and wipe my chin with my coat arm. "Think of all the jet fuel and the chemicals used to keep the food fresh. We need to make people aware of what they buy, and you can't love this planet if you don't make conscious choices. I'm sure you've got £1.50 to spare a week."

The girl sighs and her tits sigh with her. "I don't really work at the moment."

"So how come you can afford to smoke?"

"I've given up."

"What do you mean you don't *really* work?"

"I do some odd jobs. Cleaning and stuff. Cash in hand, you know."

"Then you can spare £6 a month. It's only £1.50 a week."

"That's the coffee I have every Tuesday with my friends."

"You'll make new ones," I say, averting my gaze from her nipples. "We're one big family of lovers. There are monthly sessions where we gather to meditate and send out loving messages to all living beings and …"

"Look." The girl gives me a sly smile. "You're very cute; I used to believe in that stuff too when I was younger, but I don't want to waste money on people who knock on my door in the middle of breakfast."

I want to slap her for making my knees go as weak as my voice. It's that slack attitude of hers, making me horny and angry at the same time. Looking at her is like seeing myself when I spent my days watching daytime TV and had ice-cream for breakfast. She's taking me right back to the dream state I existed in then, but there's no turning back and it's not part of my job description to hit people.

"Have a think about it," I say. "I'll come back later. What about seven?"

"You're wasting your time, sweetie" the girl says, beginning to pull the door shut. "I'm growing parsley in the back garden and that's enough for me."

"Don't you want everybody to grow their own parsley?" I ask.

"Yeah, but not everybody's got a garden."

"A lot of people have patios or window sills or balconies. We're starting a campaign about growing your own vegetables, distributing pots and soil."

"Have you got any leaflets?" she asks. I can't tell if I've won her over, of if she just wants to get on with breakfast.

"We don't do leaflets. It's a waste of paper. You can look us up on the net. Have a read at loversoftheplanet.com and I'll see you at seven."

I walk off before she gets a chance to protest.

The rain hits me like a cold shower. It's quarter past seven and I'm standing under a tree opposite the house with the blue door. My knuckles are cracked and sore from knocking for the past quarter of an hour. I bet she's gone back to bed with ear plugs in.

She's my last hope compared to the football-fan who was going to call the police or the man who set his dog on me, she was really friendly.

It feels like there's a damp towel stuffed under my coat. It was supposed to be waterproof. If I get a cold I can't work and if I can't work I won't get paid. I try to memorise what it said in the little green handbook: As a fundraiser I'm happy to be on the hourly minimum wage and accept that there's no sick-leave. I'm doing this because I love this planet and when you love someone you should be prepared to get wet for their sake.

The rain is getting heavier. I want to go home and burn the little green handbook just to keep me warm. I decide that I can make up for this day by recruiting four lovers tomorrow but, just as I'm about to go, I spot her coming round the corner, loaded down with Lidl carrier bags.

The rain doesn't seem to bother her. She's wearing her T-shirt and jeans like a bikini and walks as if she was swimming down the street. I watch as she enters the house and shuts the door behind her. I estimate how long it'll take her to unpack the groceries and when that time has elapsed I knock again. The door swings open, making me stumble backwards and grab onto the wall to steady myself. She's wearing a bath robe and her hair is like a rainforest.

"I thought you'd given up by now," she says, sounding amused rather than annoyed, leaving the door wide open. "I'm in the middle of cooking."

I follow her through the narrow hallway into a tiny square kitchen that stinks of fish. My stomach rumbles. I haven't had fish or any other meat for years. The girl shuffles over to the cooker where a line of fish fingers are hissing in the pan. I lean against the table on which the bags from Lidl are still sitting. I bet there's not a single organic or fair trade item in them. On the other hand who am I to judge: the Executive Director of Lovers of the Planet wouldn't be happy if she saw the Coke cans in my fridge.

"Did you have a look at our website?" I ask, feeling as hopeful as a school girl waiting to hear that she's passed an exam.

"No, I was shopping."

"Fish fingers is the worst kind of fish you could be eating," I say. "It's just batter."

"I thought that was a good thing, you know." The girl turns the fish fingers over with a spatula. "Not as many fish get killed as if I was having a fillet."

"Are you making fun of me?" I ask.

"No."

"Then stop talking rubbish."

"It's quite a rubbish job you've got, isn't it?" The girl turns and points at me with the spatula. One of her tits falls out of the robe, pale and big like the ostrich egg I once ate.

I look down. The rain from my coat and my hair has made a little puddle by my feet. I don't want to go back outside.

"£1.50 a week is a packet of fish fingers," I say. "Come on, you can afford to become a lover."

"Fish fingers are only 99p in Lidl," the girl says, moving closer, so close that her bare toes nudges my wet boots. "How much do you get an hour?"

"What do you mean?" The oil from the girl's raised spatula drips onto my coat. I take a step to the side.

"You deserve something better," she says, dropping the spatula which hits the floor with a crack. I open my mouth like a goldfish, but can't speak. The ostrich egg is close enough for me to lick.

"If you really want to make a difference you should go to Africa and help at a school or something," she says, taking hold of my heart-shaped badge. "How much did this cost?"

"I don't know."

"And what about your uniform?" She grabs my wrists and pins me to the table. My head is crammed between the carrier bags and I feel stiff like a frozen fish finger.

"Y-you don't have to join," I say. "Or if you do, you could cancel your membership anytime."

"Sure." The girl heaves herself on top of me. Her red tangles fall over my face and her breath is warm against my cheek.

"I can become your lover for free," she whispers in my ear.

I wriggle and kick my feet in the air, but her grip is tight. My mobile is in my inner pocket. The Executive Director told us to call the office if we experienced any trouble, but there's something about the rain smattering against the window, and the fact that I've been on my feet since the morning that makes me enter that unemployed dream state. The girl's tits are warm and heavy against my coat and are beginning to thaw me out. I close my eyes and focus on my breathing as she lets go of my wrists and unzips my uniform.

The Icebreaker

Steve Howe

☙

Micah Rushforth never ate the same thing twice. He was a colleague and friend of mine back when flexible work was the only work. We would file from the kitchen, two steaming plates in two white-gloved hands, among a tide of steaming plates in white-gloved hands, all pouring through the gaps between round tables at which the guests sat, all surging towards a waving clipboard on the horizon, the safe beacon to which we all were drawn. Sometimes we would race. The more waiters you overtook on the way the more points you racked up, and sometimes he would make me play a game which involved saying something unnerving to the guest your plate was delivered to, something like, 'I only dropped it once, sir,' or even more ridiculously, in a mock-mother sing-song voice, 'eatey-uppy your din-dins'.

"I never eat the same thing twice," Micah said, to a table of work colleagues. He had just ordered king prawns in a jam roly poly. The waiter had arched her eyebrow at first, her eyes dancing around the electronic pad, searching it for the answer to this particularly unusual request. Remembering her training, a smile appeared on her face – of course we can do that, no problem.

"What do you mean, you never eat the same thing twice?" said Sarah, "How is that possible?"

"If you're creative enough," Micah replied, looking deep into his pint of lager as if reading tea leaves, "you can completely avoid eating the same thing twice. There are countless combinations."

"But what about when you were a baby?" a man with a low, monotone voice said.

"Of course my parents didn't know of my decision as a baby," he said quickly, waiting for the ripple of laughter that normally spread, at the expense of the embarrassed speaker. The ripple did spread. "And yes, unfortunately, that does mean I'm not allowed to eat baby food again," he said, looking up to meet a louder hit of laughter with those dazzling, expectant eyes. Of course, I laughed along as if it were the first time I had heard it.

"But...what if you like something?" Sarah said, folding her red napkin into a little crushed triangle, "You can never have fish and chips or ice-cream on the beach again? A hangover fry-up?"

Micah shrugged and leaned back in his chair, like a boardroom executive about to make an important decision. "Everything is disappointing the second time around."

I silently mouthed the words with him behind my pint glass.

Due to the nature of our work, I didn't see Micah again for some time, not until a charity dinner the following week. During a break in service, he had produced a Chinese meal in a Tupperware box, which contained, among other things, chicken feet.

"Why d'you bring your own food?" a girl said, whose hair was scraped back so harshly it looked like her bun was attempting to suck in the whole of her face. "Are you a vegetarian or summin'? Or the other one, the no dairy one?"

"No," Micah replied, "I never...never eat. Never eat the same thing twice." Here he struggled, because he had just forked into his mouth a large piece of ginger. His chewing slowed like a steam engine gradually groaning to a halt.

"That's ginger," I said.

"I know," he snapped.

The girl with the scraped-back hair was looking at him intently. Micah suddenly realised that his face had been contorted into a curious scowl. A smile appeared, the steam engine fired back up, and the jaw returned to a rhythmic wrenching and unclenching of the bitter object in his mouth.

A couple of days later I was sat at home, reading as usual, the rain splattering the fat sycamore leaves just outside my window in a comforting melody. The phone rang. I picked it up and Micah was on the other end, along with a sound that was new to me. It dawned on me that he was crying.

"Andy, I didn't know who else to call," he said.

"What's up?" I said.

"There's nothing"

"What?"

"Nothing...nothing else to eat"

"What do you mean?"

"I've tried everything, every single food you can think of, every combination, every curry, stir-fry and every bloody pie. Food from all over; Welsh rarebit, haggis, squirrel brain and sea slugs. *Sea slugs* Andy. I've had desserts, tapas, confectionary, soups, stews, on toast, in a sandwich, food inside food, grilled, mashed, sautéed and smoothied."

"Surely there's something."

"Listen to me. I've tried *everything*. Yesterday I tried boiling salmon in marmite."

I looked up from the floor for a minute to take this in, out into the darkness where I knew the leaves hung heavy and sodden.

"You need to eat something," I finally said.

"I know," he sniffed, "I haven't eaten for two days. Do you know how hard that is when all you think about is food?"

"So have a dish you've had before"

"But I can't," he wailed through the receiver. It was as if a fraudster was mimicking his voice. "I never eat. Eat the..." the voice limped off into silence.

"What are you so afraid of?" I asked.

That night, Micah ate.

On a shift I saw him again; a different event, different caterers, different staff. He was hacking out a slice of staff lasagne with a big metal spoon. The way he flicked it onto a paper plate reminded me of a dinner lady serving, with laboured indifference, child after child their school meals. He walked and sat, back against the wall, behind a big group of laughing waiters. He placed the plate on the floor next to him and tucked his long legs up into his body. He glanced up and watched the group, their mouths opening and closing, eleven white plastic forks descending on eleven quivering slabs of lasagne.

Seek Alternative Route

Simon Kewin

CB

Buckley thumped his steering-wheel in frustration. Ahead, the motorway was a bank of red lights as the traffic in all three lanes came to a halt. He had been cruising comfortably along at eighty, plenty of time to get to the meeting, and now this. A red triangle lit up on his SatNav. *Congestion* it said underneath. *Seek alternative route.*

He swore. He was miles from Bracknell. Cars jostled up behind him to fill his mirror. If he wasn't at the meeting, Stephens would push through his own plans for Europe. And everyone knew what that meant.

He scrolled through the numbers on his Blackberry. O'Connor would have to state their case. A shame the man was useless. Stephens would frown and question and O'Connor would roll over.

"Hi Neil. Are you nearly here?" O'Connor sounded worried. O'Connor always sounded worried.

"I'm stuck on the bloody M4. Have you got the PowerPoint in case I'm late?"

"I've got the one you emailed on Tuesday."

"Good enough. Just make sure everyone sees it. Especially Hampton. She's the one that matters. She's a bitch but she's not stupid. If Stephens gets the nod we're dead in the water."

"They're both here already."

"Just tell her I'll be there as soon as I can." He hung up and sat for a moment, fuming with useless anger. He knew how it worked. Decisions were made beforehand, over coffee. The actual meeting was just for show. He had to get there in time.

He opened the car-door and stepped onto the motorway. It was colder than he had expected. The air tasted of fumes. At least the rain had stopped. He peered up the huddled lines of traffic. Nothing moved. He held up his arms in a shrug of disbelief.

In the middle-lane, five cars back, Slaughtered Pig pulled out the earphones of his iPod. He sighed. At least he had plenty of time. It was hours before the night's gig and they were on last anyway.

He leafed through the tattered road atlas to find the night's venue, the *Independent Chapel* in Reading. They had played there once before, years ago, when they were up and coming. Did that mean they were on their way back down now? Or, the thought that troubled him more and more, did it mean they'd never gone anywhere in the first place?

Up ahead, a suit had opened the door of his silver Mercedes and was gesturing at the traffic as if the whole thing had been staged to inconvenience him. He would have been powerfully built once, a rugby-player type, but now the curve of his belly protruded farther than his chest. Heart-attack shape. Pig grinned. The Merc had a personalized number plate, NE1L 3, the 1 written so that it looked like the letter I. Wanker. Did it rankle with him that he couldn't afford NE1L 2 or NE1L 1? He had cruised by a mile or two back. Now they were almost together. It felt like a victory of sorts.

Pig rolled a twig-like fag, watching the man. All that singing and shouting. The band hadn't really changed anything had they? The world was still run by people like this, executives and bankers ruining everything. Still, he had tried and that was something.

The suit *would* have a mobile, though. Perhaps he could borrow it. Let the band know where he was. He waited a few moments then, with no sign of the traffic moving, stepped down from the van.

Buckley watched the low-life slam the door of his Transit van. On the side it said, painted in crude red letters, *Catharsis World Tour*. This was all he needed. The guy looked like he *lived* in the vehicle. His head was shaved, his ears and eyebrows studded with metal, his tee-shirt ripped and stained. Several teeth were missing. Lost in some brawl, no doubt. Or resisting arrest.

"Looks like a bad one," the low-life said as he approached, indicating the lines of traffic with a nod of his head. "Gets worse every day, eh?"

Establish a rapport. Identify a shared problem. It was nicely done.

"Too much traffic on the roads," said Buckley.

"I'm Slaughtered Pig."

"Slaughtered Pig?"

"Stage name. From an early review. *The singer grunts and squeals like a slaughtered pig.* You can call me Terry."

"Terry Pig?"

The man grinned. "Terry Burns."

Wasters like this made him laugh; going about thinking the world owed them a living. "And your band's called Catharsis, right?" Buckley prided himself on being able to put people at their ease.

"That's it. Punk Rock stalwarts."

"Like the Sex Pistols?"

"Kinda. That's ancient history. We're more thrash. Grindcore, you know?"

"My son's in a band."

"What does he play?"

"Guitar."

"No, I mean what sort of music. Indie, dub, trance, metal, what?"

"Well, rock. You know, pop."

"What bands he into?"

"Well, I took him to see Springsteen at Twickenham last year. The Boss, you know? Fantastic. The guy works so hard. Played for over three hours."

"I'm not really a fan."

"I've got some in the car. If we're stuck here long you can listen to some." It was meant as a joke. He regretted it as soon as he'd said it. There were still no cars moving. Everyone had turned their engines off. The only sound was the ticking of cooling metal.

Christ. All he'd wanted was to borrow the guy's phone, not move in with him.

Although actually, now that he saw the suit up close, he was beginning to feel sorry for him. You could see how unhappy he was. The features of his face were lost in fat, all those meals in expensive restaurants, networking, making deals. A life of meetings and sucking the cock of the next suit up. It was Pig's idea of hell.

"Going anywhere important?" asked Pig.

"Meeting. You?" The suit wasn't really interested, of course; his eyes wandered even as he asked.

"Gig."

"Ah."

Up and down the motorway, other drivers climbed out of their cars, like animals emerging from hibernation. Parents herded children off to the hard shoulder to squat awkwardly in the grass. An illuminated sign above the carriageway woke up, displaying the single word *Congestion*. Pig flicked the end of his fag to the ground. This late in the year, it was already beginning to get dark. The sun was just a formless smudge of white light in the sky behind them, giving off no heat.

"Fancy a cup of tea?" he said. Scum he may be but the guy looked like he needed it.

"You have tea?"

"In a flask."

The suit nodded and turned to gaze up the motorway.

When Pig returned, the man was back in his car, door wide open, talking in angry tones to someone called O'Connor. He indicated the passenger seat with a nod of his head. Pig, grinning at being told what to do, walked around the car. The Merc would be warm at least. The leather of the seat was soft. The suit finished his conversation and slammed the phone back into its cradle.

"Not good?" asked Pig.

"Not good. Two years work down the drain. Apparently Hampton loved Stephens' plans. Said ours were *ambitious*. Ambitious! Bloody cow." He was staring out of the windscreen, not really seeing Pig. His tie was loose now and rings of sweat crept out from his armpits. Pig poured tea into a plastic cup and handed it to him.

"Black, no sugar I'm afraid."

The suit turned to look at him, as if only then aware of his presence in the car.

"Thanks," he said, taking the cup.

"So, you lost a deal or something?"

"A big deal."

For a moment, Pig thought that was all he was going to say. Then he carried on.

"It's curtains for the whole division, now. We're dead in the fucking water. Two years, maybe three, the whole thing will go tits-up. Without Europe we're just a backwater. We're fucking toast."

Pig sipped his tea, letting him rant. The guy needed to rant. He understood that feeling well enough. It was pretty much his entire act. He sat back, enjoying the enfolding softness of the car seat.

And here was the terrible truth. Although he had been the singer with Catharsis for ten years now, living the life, and although he had the words *Punk Rock 'Til I Die* tattooed across his chest in red and black, sometimes, rattling back home at three in the morning, he fantasised about having a car like this. And a

41

house with heating. And holidays. And a pension to look forward to rather than poverty. He actually found himself wishing he had a pension. Sweet fucking Jesus, how rock 'n roll was that?

He knew he couldn't be the singer in Catharsis for ever. But what were the alternatives? He had lost too many friends to the twin evils of heroin and the rat-race. Sometimes it seemed one of them would get him in the end too. Heroin was quicker but the other was just as effective. Worse really. The body survived but the soul died. A year, or two, or ten if they were strong, and they started to believe what they were doing mattered. That it was what they *were*.

He sometimes thought about all the kids who had come to see them play in the old days. You still saw a few, maybe, standing at the back. But most had been lost, that whole generation. It was like the First World War or something.

Pig poured them both more tea. "Listen, I've brought our latest CD. If you give it a go I'll suffer Bruce Fucking Springsteen. Deal?"

The suit had visibly sagged since the phone call.

"Sure," he said.

They sat in silence, listening to *Darkness on the Edge of Town*. Buckley had forgotten how much he loved the album. Hadn't listened to it for years, not properly. There was no comparison to Catharsis. Dear God, that had been like someone sandpapering his brain. Still, you had to admire what Pig had done, making a career out of such a lack of talent. It was actually impressive. He was his own boss.

Buckley looked at the clock on the dashboard. They had been here for two hours. What time would he finally get home? What would Janice say when he did? She was used to it, of course. All the nights and weekends away. The trips abroad. He had worked bloody hard.

His gaze returned to the photo he had found tucked inside the Springsteen case. It was what, twenty-five years old? He had transplanted the CD from car to car, promising himself he would listen to it again. The colours of the picture were washed out but the detail was clear. What had happened to them all, those young men grinning and posing like idiots for the camera? Big Bob, always in his Motörhead tee-shirt. Gram holding Andy in a head-lock, pretending to strangle him. Buckley standing behind them, holding up two open cans of beer.

They had been to a rock festival, drunk warm bitter for three days straight and slept in Big Bob's battered Datsun when it rained. The memories were vivid. Sometimes he could remember nothing at all of whole years since then. The photo was taken at a service station on the M6. They had laughed at the disapproving glares of the other motorists, the parents ushering children out of their path.

Big Bob had a guitar and Gram played the drums. They talked about starting a band. He had forgotten about that. He hadn't spoken to any of them for years. He wondered what they would say to each other if they met again.

A police officer in a yellow jacket walked down the line of cars, stopping to speak to each driver. Buckley pressed the button to lower his window. Her name tag identified her as *Gough*. Young, but she looked like she could handle just about anything.

"Everything okay here, gentlemen?"

"We're fine, officer," Buckley replied. "When will we be moving?"

"Going to be a while I'm afraid." She must have told the story a hundred times but she remained polite. "There's been a bad accident three miles ahead. Fire has damaged the carriageway. We're waiting for cranes. If there's an emergency we can get you out but otherwise it's best you stay with your vehicle." She glanced at the Volvo behind them. "We'll provide food and blankets. It'll be cold later."

"It's okay," said Pig. "Got loads of blankets in the van. Heater doesn't work. In the winter I get ice on the *inside*."

"This isn't your vehicle, sir?"

"No. I'm in the Transit back there."

Gough looked away for a moment.

"Could you get them, sir?"

"What now?"

"Please."

Pig grinned. "Sure."

When he was gone, the officer leaned in and spoke quietly.

"This man is not causing you a problem is he?"

"We're just talking," said Buckley.

She didn't look convinced. "Well, if you need us, just phone 999. You'd be surprised what goes on when people are stranded on a motorway overnight."

"I will, officer, thank you."

She stepped back and wrote something in her notebook. Pig smiled at her as he returned, holding a bundle of blankets. They filled the car with the smell of dust.

"She thought I was mugging you didn't she?" said Pig.

"She did."

"Happens all the time. Mind you, this *is* a nice car.

He was joking, Buckley could see that. His ferocious appearance was all show.

Buckley leaned back. "Feel free. It hardly matters now."

"Well, maybe later," said Pig.

"Listen, do you want to phone anyone?"

"Uh, yeah, that would be good actually, thanks."

Buckley listened as Pig argued with someone in his band over who would do the singing. If 'singing' was the right word.

So Greg could manage the vocals could he? The man had all the stage-presence of an armchair. Jesus.

Pig tried to put them out of his mind, think about something else. A tune had been buzzing round in his head for hours. He had the chord progression. E minor, A minor, D, E minor. Then E, C, D, for the chorus. The thing was, however much he played the song in his mind, he couldn't make it sound like Catharsis. It was more … reflective. It was still noisy; it wasn't fucking Springsteen for Christ's sake. But it wasn't a song Greg would like. He had quite a collection of them now. Enough for an album.

"So your band can manage without you?"

"So they say."

"Sounds like there are musical differences."

Pig laughed.

"Thing is, I'm the only one left from the original line-up. They think I've gone soft."

"Didn't sound like it to me."

"They're just young."

"But they can't kick you out surely? That must be against the agreement."

"There is no contract. This is a punk band, not a corporation."

"Well, I wouldn't let them walk all over me."

"No. I'm sure." He really didn't need advice from the man. "So what about you? Where do you go now this division of yours is fucked?"

"Oh, something will come up. Irons in fires, you know?"

"I could hear how much you hate them. You should get away. I don't know, be your own boss. Whatever."

Buckley looked at him but didn't reply.

They ate the sandwiches and chocolate provided for them in silence. It was late now, nearly eleven. They still hadn't moved. He had phoned Janice to tell her he wouldn't be getting home any time soon. She had sounded tired.

He had been starting the car occasionally to give them some heat, but now he was huddled under one of Pig's blankets. They had both been lost in their thoughts for a long time.

"So maybe you should go solo too," said Buckley. "Strike out on your own."

Pig, not even opening his eyes, only grunted in reply.

At two in the morning, Constable Gough walked back down the line of vehicles. She shone her torch into the Mercedes. The businessman and the skinhead were sound asleep, the car's seats fully reclined, a tattered blanket covering each of them. They breathed in unison. Shaking her head, she walked on to check the young family in the Volvo.

Four hours later, they finally began to creep forwards. Car and van overtook each other repeatedly as the three lanes of traffic built up speed. The sky ahead glowed with golden light.

Pig's engine made its usual grinding noises, but he soon hit sixty. He tossed the road atlas into the van's foot well. He knew where he was going now. He would come off the motorway at the next junction, go round and come back on. There was no longer any need to get to Reading.

Buckley, in the outside lane, stretched some life back into his arms and shoulders. It was good just to be moving. He glanced out of his side-window, away from the narrow funnel of the motorway, out over fields and woods, catching glimpses of distant buildings in the half-light. He thought about his plans. He could be home in a couple of hours. He had a lot of calls to make. He and Janice needed to talk.

He watched Pig come off the motorway, his van ascending the slip road, curving up and away. Buckley grinned at the sight of him in his mirror and accelerated forwards.

She Would Have Made a Fine Crusader's Wife; Keeping Just Account, Breaking the Necks of Hares, Their Poachers

Helen McClory

❧

Aida lay on the mat in her tent sprawled against the body of her K.O.'d lover, her body separate now and struggling to cope. Not all the way starved of breath; wracked more with that anxious euphoria she'd experienced on getting stuck under a ledge of sea-rock, her snorkel a useless straw piping water in gulps. This heady taste, not salt, was of the latex air in deflating balloons. Everything slowly going back to humid and dim. She could feel Tick's chest rising and falling evenly under her soft belly.

Side effect, she thought. Gleeful over-exertion under a mad-dog sun. Leading to peach-tongued, orgasmic dehydration, and reeling while horizontal. She wouldn't be drawn into that again. It felt like *gusto*, a romantic bilge her mother had harped on, dangling her brush over another canvas of watery cascades. *L'esprit de coeur! Byron! Sublime! Turner! I think a little wood-sprite tree, don't you, petal?* Before the inevitable nuzzling in of one of her ever-dreary rainbows. Aida looked up terms, and scoffed. *L'esprit de corps*, wasn't that what she had meant? Morale, stupid mother. Belief in one's own goals, concrete steps.

Fucking the new neighbour and then a second time in the same way outdoors in the brush was not in any way *gusto, al fresco*. That was meals, usually tomato salad. It just happened, and was biological; a good and justifiable sequence of responses. The aftermath was troublesome, still. Vision of a river and the odd little Freudian – not Tick, a sudden stranger – peering over her as she writhed. Aida held tight her packet of sanity and unsaid vows, and had great reserves of missionary purposefulness. The teeniest psychic vulnerability – air deprivation or not – must be dealt with.

However, now, scuttle metaphors, banish mothers, and take up a clean and practical snooze.

A goat, a duppy and a walnut tree the more you beat them the better they be

Caroline Moir

☙

Only it's difficult now to find a walnut tree. But I know where there is one. The walnuts stain your hands ochre and grime your fingernails, and the odour of iodine accompanies you as you cup them home. Beating a goat is just silly. The billy at the end of our road, his testy, randy, tang comes to meet you before you see him. He puts his feet high up on the wall and snickers his lips in a grin. His eyes are yellow opal sliced by the line of his pupils, his beard tremors with his desire to come over, over to your side. Look what big horns he's got – all the better to poke you with, my dear.

And you can't beat a duppy though you can call one up with beer and money thrown down on its grave ground and send it out to haunt your enemy until your enemy goes away.

*

Once was a woman arrive in this old island. She going to live her life here. With her man who work the plantation, with her two babies and ones to come, the born islanders. Adventure. In paradise, she say. But it was three year after the big war, the world war two. The sugar, it hadn't recover, it never recover. Wasn't money 'nough for 'nother manager. That was one wrong ting. And a bad man mash the dog Bellady down, what the little girl and boy say. That was two wrong ting. But the nice doctor come. He make Bellady better. And the woman is heavy with baby. That is two good ting, the daddy say.

Also there was the maid-girl for the children, late afternoons spent by copper green seas sifting white sand for tiny pink cowries, fresh nut milk to sweeten the harsh rum. Life was not too horrid.

The woman got pains. The doctor come and haul her feet in air and pull with his tongs and take the baby away. There be no more babies he say.

After, the woman smelt the duppy. Between sun down and cock crow it lingered in the porch. Left its whiff – oily nut, rancid, nostril-whickering goat, iodine from the seaweed it trailed. Every night, she said. It came every night.

The woman and her husband and the two children left the island. They set sail on a top-heavy lake boat, because all the ships been taken to the navy or sunk in world war two. They steamed across the deep sea back from where they had come. And the woman threw their last beer bottle into the long, dark swell of the waves. Stoppered inside was a note. Please send money.

A joke, she said, happy to escape.

*

But you don't beat a duppy, a goat or a walnut tree.

Toreador

Christina Murphy

❧

I am thinking

My brother painted these words above his bed shortly after his third suicide attempt. He used the sienna and gold from his paint-by-number set. The third attempt was a hanging, with the pulley at such an angle that the rope gave way at the last moment and dropped my brother safely to the ground. Now he has a red welt around his neck. "Someday you'll go too far," my mother said to him, "and then you'll be sorry."

When I talk to my brother, I try to figure out the causes of his behavior. He seems normal enough, has the proper interests in sports and girls. The only unusual thing about him that I can see is his aquarium, which is full of hand-carved wooden fish.

"We will name the fish," he says, taking them out of the tank. "Jell-O, Minnesota, Hiawatha, and Lee."

Lee is an angelfish, as best as I can tell, though his stripes are not white and black but burgundy and orange. My brother puts Lee into a tiny wooden cart and moves him back and forth along the edge of the desk. "Oh, well," my brother says when the cart tips over and Lee hits the floor. "Oh, well." Then he climbs into bed and reads.

When I get tired of being with my brother, I go into the kitchen. My mother is frying eggs. I sit with her while she drinks her coffee.

"Today is becoming like every other day," she says. She takes a sip of coffee from a white porcelain mug and leaves a half moon of lipstick on the rim.

I don't want to be with my mother. She depresses me. I wrap one of the fried eggs in tin foil and put it in my pocket. It gives a warm feeling to my chest. I go out the back door to the woods to sit by a berry bush and eat my egg and dream of Arlene.

Arlene is my girlfriend. She works the counter at Dairy Heaven in a pink uniform covered with clouds. Saturday nights I go to see her work, and the place is often so full of people that Arlene scoops and serves until midnight. Afterwards, when Arlene is cleaning up, and the only light in Dairy Heaven is a puff of neon yellow from the Banana Split sign, I sit in the back and eat a triple cup of dark chocolate ice cream. Cocoa Killer is my favorite, though Arlene always tells me to try Devil's Cake Dream.

My mother comes out the back door. "Bobby," she says, "Bobby?" She turns on the sprinkler, and an arc of beads fills the yard. She looks down the path and sees me sitting by the berry bush. "Oh, there you are," she says. "I need you to come in and help me move some furniture so I can clean the living room."

"In a minute. I'm eating," I say to her.

She nods her head and goes back into the house. The sprinkler continues to fling water across the yard.

I help my mother move the sofa. There are dust balls and pennies underneath. My mother tells me I can have the pennies. I leave them on the floor.

When I get bored, I walk to the Stop 'n Go. I buy a Milky Way and eat it while sitting on a fire hydrant near the bank. Arlene and I have been on this street many times. One day the high school marching band went by, and we followed the band through the town and into the park. The band played the *Star Spangled Banner* and *God Bless America*. I bought some hot dogs and a balloon for Arlene with buttercups painted on it and a small red heart stamped in the center. We sat on a park bench and fed the hot dog buns to the pigeons, until the wind blew and the pigeons scattered, landing in some bushes near the path behind us.

I buy two more Milky Ways at the Stop 'n Go and spend the afternoon playing video games at Aladdin's Arcade. When I get home, I find out that my brother has bought a bird. A cockatiel with jet black eyes and a streak of peachblow on the tips of his feathers.

"He can talk," my brother says. "He can say 'toreador'. Listen!"

Tic tic tuh. Tic tic tuh.

"You hear it?" my brother says.

"Yeah, toreador. That's great," I say.

That evening, my mother makes pancakes shaped like pyramids. She puts a ribbon of cane syrup on them and serves them to us on blue and yellow plates. It makes me sick to stick my fork into the pancakes and watch the syrup ooze out the sides. "Why aren't you eating?" my mother asks, but I ignore her. It's too much trouble to explain.

I help my mother with the dishes, scraping globs of pancake mix into a trash bag under the sink. My brother reads the sports page. He likes the Chicago Cubs.

I have nothing to do, so I tell them goodnight and go into the bedroom I share with my brother. His fish are out of the aquarium again. This time he has painted little green triangles on their faces.

I get into bed. Soon, my brother comes in and climbs into the bunk bed above me.

Tic tic tuh, the bird says, sitting on his perch in the corner, *tic tic tuh*.

My brother turns off the lights and plays the harmonica he found in a vacant lot. Most of the reeds are broken, so it makes an eerie, wispy sound like the wind in an old house.

The harmonica is quiet now. The bird moves along his perch. I wonder if soon there will be another suicide attempt.

Origami

Kirsty Neary

ര

Marion perches on her favourite chair in the smoking room, tearing thin strips of paper from a hospital welcome pack. Each blank tongue she neatly folds, tucking in torn edges, before rolling a narrow tube. The wreckage of a garden party sprawls across the coffee table: bright confetti of torn helpline pamphlets sifting their way to the floor; a broken picket fence of paper pipes reeling between the toadstool spread of half-empty coffee cups. She keeps her eyes fixed on her hands as the door creaks open, holds her gaze even as the laminated chair to her left expels a puff of chemical dust. A clearing of throat, ruffling of papers and a few long breaths intimate a settling down. A taking of stock. Finally the newcomer speaks. A voice from the underground. Squashed tin cans and rusted spoons.

"Marion, sweetie. It's been too long."

Marion's shoulders jerk up to her ears, then curve as she leans in to shelter her torso. The smirk playing about her lips is mirrored in Lucy's own mouth. The hospital's success rates weren't making much of an impression, so far. And so here they were. Reunions with former inmates were a strange kind of comfortable: so many secrets already passed between them both a blessing and a curse in terms of selecting strains of etiquette. There's no rush to reply; instead, both women give over to the thick tick of the plastic clock over the television. Things move at a different pace than on the outside: the sedated find extended pauses necessary to slap occurrences in concrete. To take a measure of one's thoughts, feelings, presuppositions and possible actions, as drilled by the doctors and their interminable worksheets.

"How rude," says Lucy, finally. "Where's the welcome home for the troops?"

Lucy's not too bothered about the form and content of a response; a syllable, a sigh, would be enough. There's just a real need to hear *something*. To confirm suspicions gathered by her senses: that she's really back. She's not ready to unpack, yet, not ready to settle into her room, take a look around the ward, mark changes.

The smoking room's a port of call even for those who don't smoke: always the same, reassuringly bare of therapeutic worksheets, fluorescent health posters, scuttling nurses clutching clipboards to their chests with an air of privileged information. Here, there's nothing so important that can't wait twenty puffs, no immediate need to get a grip. No panic over the fact that the plastic wrapping on the couch under her fingertips feels as substantial as a handful of cobwebs; the mute light glancing from the rims of the amassed coffee cups fluttering her line of sight, knocking back attempts to gain horizons, limits, edges. Stepping back into the swing of things will take time. There's plenty of that in here.

Marion folds and rolls a further three tubes of paper, bringing the count up to a nice neat number divisible by ten and two and five and three. Under-lid glances at Lucy affirm her suspicions; the girl's been pushing it further and harder. Time for a pleasantry.

"So you're back," she says. She sounds impressed, near-awed at the thought of the *outside* concerned. As though Lucy's returned from a mission of mercy building wells in darkest Africa; hiking up mountains in the Andes; uncovering Incan ruins. Finding out more. More than this. More than that which digs violet trenches into her eye sockets.

"Yeah. How's it going?"

There's no protocol for such a situation. Just a reversal. This time it's Lucy looking like hell, dragged backward by the hair through every dead-end alley in the maze of the city; Marion slightly plumped and gently flushed by what looks to be at least six weeks of inpatient.

"Fucking splendid. Not the point. Where've you been and why the hell are you back?"

"I could ask the same thing of you, Marion."

Brief silence; the sick girl and the not-so-sick girl tabulate degrees of decay. Marion makes no effort to screen her disappointment; it's a far more appropriate reaction than the twinge of envy battering at the inner rims of her ribcage. Lucy's had one more go of it; another shot at pushing every limit her imagination can supply. One failing on the part of the doctors was a sure-fire means of reinforcing the pleasure-centric benefits of sickness over health. What should, could the patients *do* with all that rude health?

"Did you have time to pack this time? Bring a decent stash of cigarettes?" Marion finally asks; there's no arguing with currency, more readily swapped than horror stories.

"Aye." Lucy digs a deck out from a pocket of her paint-spattered jeans.

"Not those Silk Cut low-tar things, still?"

"Aye."

"What the fuck, Lucy – I thought you'd have gotten over that little health kick of yours."

"I'm too used to them now. You know how it is...you can't go back."

The latter phrase wraps a tune, Lucy's voice rising up to meet the prerequisite positive outlook required on a programme of recovery. An in-joke tar-thick with blackest humour.

"Neither you can; what's the idea? They're easier to quit, or something?"

"I thought since they're rotten I'd smoke less of them."

"How's that working out for you?"

"Ha-ha...smoking even more just to get a buzz."

"Always the way."

"As I'll no doubt be reminded."

Marion picks her key, a sing-along cursor bouncing along the top of her words.

"Give it time. You know how it works – you're meant to get your bearings, first. Come to terms with your circumstances...get to know and appreciate your surroundings..." Marion sweeps her hand across the smoking room, taking in the safety-glassed French windows, the shades of grey constituting the staff car park outside, the starving winter briars, the brew of smoke issuing from the stacks just visible over the top of the ten-foot wall.

"Lap of luxury, eh?" drawls Lucy, chucking a half-pack of Silk Cut Marion's way.

"Yeah...who needs holiday homes in the Med or penthouses in New York when you can take a motorway turn right on into Seven Oaks? Full board, maid service, *organized fun* and, eh... more *security* than the Pentagon?"

"You've really been working on that gratitude list," says Lucy, raising her brows. She lifts a hand to the left one; she's still not used to the bare patch left after the singeing incident. "I can tell. What you going for with all that silver lining? Earrings? Bracelets? A new dinette set?"

Marion shrugs, removes a cigarette from the pack, holds it up alongside one of her own rolls of paper. Almost an exact match. Perfect. She lights the cigarette, pulling a face. Might as well be smoking newspaper, for all the nip in the hit.

"Sounds like your own could use a bit of work. If you're back in here."

"That, Marion dear, is between each patient and their carefully appointed key worker," says Lucy, no inflection in the reply. She's pulled between extremes: on the one hand, the relish of secrecy; on the other, the need to reveal all, make it real, make damn sure she can still pin scraps of language onto the mess in her head. Another casual pause gives Marion time to decide whether or not to push it.

"Hmmm....these are as foul as I remember," drawls Marion, watching the smoke rise up to join the clot around the light fixtures, motes of dust glittering in the pale haze from the burglar-proof floodlights outside.

"Ach, they're alright. Good for..." Lucy makes a mock about-face, pretending to check over her shoulder, cupping her ears around the slightest of staff-sounds. "...spliffs, Marion. Means you can't taste anything but the grass..."

Marion frowns, stretches out her right leg without uncurling her spine from its taut comma. Hooking over another small card table, she transfers all the empties from one to another, freeing up space for her craft. She begins arranging her paper tubes in groups of five, then three, each grouping at right angles to the last until she has a Tower of Pisa; a stairway to nowhere.

"No offense, but I doubt you're back in here for indulging in purely herbal refreshment."

Lucy coughs, growls, sprawls back on the couch in a creak of wipe-clean plastic. She stares at the ceiling, trying to pick out the scallops around the edge of the room from behind the pale curtain of smog. Formal drills from last time remind her to check herself before a reaction; people, she's been told, are rarely as careful with words as they could be. Still, there are too may loose threads hanging from Marion's observation.

"Do I...do I look *that* bad?"

Marion begins placing her paper tubes neatly into a shoebox granted, after some less than dignified pleading, from the art therapy team. There's no way around it if, as promised, she's to speak only the truth.

"Lucy...it's not up to me to pass judgement."

"Nobody else will. Tell me."

"You look like...you look like you've done pretty much everything they told you *not* to if you wanted to stay out of here."

Lucy nods, carefully. Any sudden movements of the head seem to send her brain drumming in her skull like a joint boiling in a soup-pot. Logical thoughts bursting on the surface even as they alight. Every time she moves to flick her cigarette into the ashtray, the tapes wrapping the bandages around her forearms whisper her very own personal truth.

"I did. And more. I wanted to get it right, this time."

"You not tired, yet?" asks Marion. "Not that I'm the poster child for recovery, here, but I wasn't expecting us to meet again quite so soon."

"Tired? Tired...I'm always tired, Marion. It's like....it's like every sound I've ever made is playing back over and over in my head. All at the same time. It's too loud...I haven't slept properly since...since I left here, funnily enough."

Marion gazes out from under a fringe of sleep-clogged lashes, getting it. Their eyes meet across the room, each permitting a shallow grin. Another hospital in-joke; when they'd adjoining rooms, they'd meet in the hall after they'd been given their sleep medication and attempt to fit as much talk as possible into the twenty-odd minutes before they began to slur and sink. A game; trying to show the shrinks they'd still a grasp on what it meant to retain ownership of their words, their bodies.

"Those were the days, eh..? That why you went back on it?"

Lucy shrugs, allowing the *it* concerned to flood the room, an amorphous cloud of possibilities assuming whichever weight or shape or texture the individual user required at the time.

"Yeah...no....maybe. I don't know. All I wanted was not to feel so...close. To everything. Like...all these little pieces belonging to me were all demanding my attention, all at the one time...when you take control, do something *else,* everything moves into place. Gets small enough to fit into your line of sight."

Marion flinches at the slight hitch in Lucy's voice. There were places for tears – in Seven Oaks, there had to be – but the smoking room wasn't one of them. She lifts the box of tubes and once more sets about placing them on the table, trying for words, this time. *Yes, no, maybe. Light, space, colour. Love, hate, anarchy.* T-shirts and bumper stickers. Steering well clear of the axioms padding the walls in the wards upstairs. Hanging on to the pause, the deepening of breath as Lucy gathers herself together.

"What are you doing, anyway?" Lucy asks, snorting and tugging at the front of her blouse, making a show of flaring her fingers as she lights up another cigarette.

"Playing," says Marion, sharp with irony. "The docs were handing out these flashcards with craft ideas. Colouring in, making greetings cards, knitting, that kind of thing."

"Kiddy scissors," hisses Lucy, "Plastic needles. Fuck, they don't have a clue, do they?"

"Whatever keeps us busy, I guess."

"So this is...what? Origami?"

"Kind of. I kept fucking up the swans and flowers and stuff, so...I like these. You get them all the same size, all nice and neat, and then...I dunno, make stuff."

Lucy rises slowly from the couch, drops down into the seat next to Marion. She peers into the shoebox, withdraws a tidy stack of envelopes the size of four postage stamps laid out in a square.

"What's with these?" she asks, knowing full well.

"Wraps. It's all I know how to make."

"Haven't they noticed? Your, uh...signature pieces?"

"Makes sense to me," says Marion. "Occupational therapy, right? Something to do with your hands, to keep them off...the bad shit. I figure, why the hell not? Like those fake plastic cigarettes you get for when you're trying to quit. Keeps the damage below the wrists."

Lucy trails a finger along the backbone of an H picked out in tubes; the rest of the word yet to be formed, then snatches her hand back, not yet accustomed to the sight of her gauze bracelets.

"Oh. Cool. I guess. What's this one gonna be, then?"

"Oh, I don't know, Lucy!" says Marion, injecting a school teacher's saccharine into every syllable. "Could be all sorts of things, couldn't it? Hate. Hurt. Heroin. Harm. What do *you* think, Lucy? What would be the *best* words to come from this period of self-dedicated time? Remember to *reflect*. Does the outcome match up to your *intent...*?"

"Hernia. Haemorrhage. Hedonism...?"

Marion finally raises her head from her chest to meet Lucy's eye; it's a case of laughing or crying, and can only be a good sign that they each plump for the former. Marion holds a palm up in a pause, snickering under her breath. Lucy watches as she arranges the tubes into *HAPPY*. Lucy cracks up, leans forward, provides a word of her own. *HEALTHY. HOPE.* Neither permits headspace to the ward-wide ban on self-mockery. *HISTORY* has far too many connotations; medical, admissions, abuses, repetitions.

"If Diana were here, we'd have *HOLY* before too long," drawls Lucy, remembering the God-fearing manic-depressive who'd had the room down the hall the last time she'd been in.

"Wait till you've been to dinner, or the nurses' station. Diana's back with a vengeance, sweetie. So's Gavin, if you're interested."

"Christ. One big, happy family, here, eh?"

"Hmmm...what about the obvious, then? *HOSPITAL*? Too long? Clumsy on the Os?"

Lucy folds her arms and sinks back into the seat; working on not shaking her head, working on thinking before she speaks.

"Marion..."

"Hmmm?"

"What are we doing? I mean, seriously. I'm glad you're having fun and all, but...paper tubes and fake wraps? Playing fucking...*Sesame Street?* Is that all we're good for?"

Marion curbs the urge to grab her fellow patient by the padded wrists; noting the discrepancy between *doing* and the unvoiced *doing HERE.*

"Lucy, I don't think either of us are in the position to be making demands. We fucked up again, no? Dangers to ourselves?"

"I don't see how stupid little pieces of paper are gonna make the slightest bit of difference."

"They don't," says Marion. "It's just...sounds strange, but...you can do with *these* what you can't with all those...bits in your head. They do what they're told. Stay where they're put. And if nothing comes up, well..."

She holds up the box. Lucy snorts and lights a cigarette, half of the last one still smouldering in the ashtray.

"I still don't get it."

Marion loses her temper, voice pitching up to a mockery of a sitcom teen, steeped in scorn.

"There's nothing to get. Do you think I'm *enjoying* myself, here? That this is, like, the most amazingly entertaining and fulfilling thing *ever?*"

"Of course not. I just...there's got to be something *else.*"

This time, Marion does reach over to touch, gently circling Lucy's wrists with her fingers.

"Yeah. Yeah, Lucy. I can see you've got that all worked out."

"Fuck off, Marion. You're just..."

A rummage in the box, a flutter of fingers between paper tubes. Their eyes meet, briefly, before parting, embarrassed.

Marion wishes she weren't so pleased to see her friend; not in here. Lucy works to call up walls between herself and why she's back. Marion helps. Best of all, Lucy would never have to say so out loud. Never have to explain or tabulate or strip to pieces for ulterior motives. Never have to write it on a worksheet.

"I'm what?"

Lucy moves her arm to reveal her word, taking her time, squeezing the muscles of her forearms up against the taut wrappers. It's the least of what she'll have to get used to.

"*HILARIOUS*,"

"I'm in town all week."

"Makes two of us."

"*HALLE-fucking-LEUIA?*"

"Jeez. Give me strength."

Rock-a-Bye

Valerie O'Riordan

❧

I said I'd get the fucking fags meself. Useless cunt, Theo, nose in a hanky. The hearse was stopped at the lights anyway and the driver was reading the *Mirror*; I strutted past in me tight black skirt and gave him the finger on the way back, Silk Cut between me lips, thumb to the lighter. I gave Theo the rest of the pack and he used mine to light his. With the smoke making our eyes leak, there was no talking for the rest of the drive.

The cemetery was massive – Wembley, Old Trafford, the Emirates and the Stadium of fucking Light all in one, late September sunlight bouncing off white marble angels with little kiddies' faces. I wore me Ibiza shades. The grass was dead neat before the stones, like toy lawns, and I pictured dwarves and midgets sitting out, portable tellies balanced on the marble slabs. It was fine weather for a picnic. Theo pushed me to move faster and I shoved back at him. I didn't want to bang into the back of the coffin or chat to the sweaty priest shuffling alongside with his hands in his pockets. The Elvis-ish wave of his hair and the honky-tonk red face – Nashville, I thought, Father Tennessee. I laughed out loud.

"Jesus, Nat," hissed Theo, and I scrunched it in – the laughing. Like Shona, if I told her to shut it when she giggled during the soaps or when I was on the phone. She'd snort and go scarlet, hands to her face. Robin, I'd call her – little Robin Red Face, like the bird the cat left on the windowsill last Christmas. She hadn't laughed then.

The service was dead quick. Everyone shook the held-out hands – more Theo's than mine, though, and some of them didn't look at me once. Old colleagues, school-yard mums. Whispering instead, off behind the cars, and around me there was this dip in the sound, like it was me at the bottom of the dug-out hole, not Shona, and they were all leaving me behind. I wanted to shout, it was a fucking accident, a fucking allergy, and I wanted to claw them with muddy fingernails, press the dirt, Shona's dirt, into their dry-cleaned suits, but Theo had me by the arm and squeezed. It's all right, Nat, he said with his fingers.

I don't know. It could've happened anywhere – in school or at me ma's or at Theo's step-dad's, but it didn't. It was in me own house. I'd had me glass of wine and Shona was off to bed, so with Theo on nights, I had another glass and the last box of chocolates left over from Christmas. And then she was up again and wailing, nightmares and bogeymen, so we cuddled on the sofa and shared the last few choccies. She was quiet and tired at first, and then leaned over and puked onto the good rug. The screaming. And then it was down on the carpet and not breathing. And I couldn't find the phone, could I – battery dead in the handset and the mobile not charged, so I had to go next door, and Pam Carson made the call. In her statement she said I was unfit. Theo went round and beat twenty shades of shit outta her fella, but there's the hearing coming up anyway, and now me own ma won't come round.

We went to the village hall after the burial for vol-au-vents and cocktail sausages and the crates of fizzy pink wine we'd gotten on offer from Aldi. I stood out in the carpark and smoked through the rest of the packet of Silk Cut. I could see the graveyard wall over the road and I pictured Shona, if she were here, looking for attention, posing that way she did with one hand on her cheek and the other on her hip, lips pushed out like she was smudging lipstick on the stale air in the stuffy hall. I wasn't crying, because if I cried she'd wash away in the salty flow of it. But the smoke made me breath catch in me throat and I felt dizzy.

Theo came out and put his arm around me. "I got yeh a drink," he said. "And cheese on a stick." I closed me eyes. I could see the falling sun roaring orange in browns and reds inside me skull, and feel the heat of the day pushing at me. "Give us a fag," he said, and we smoked until the noise in me head dropped off like a radio plugged out. Theo hummed me rock-a-bye and there were the tears.

A Child in Paris

Robert Peett

ߔ

Near Chateau Rouge where gendarmes eddy round long vans, caressing guns like teenagers stroking spots, I lived on the top floor of an old house in a post-colonial street. Black-clad concierges sat on wooden chairs, gossiping and watching Algerians saunter and smoke. One evening there was a knock at my door. A wide-eyed woman I didn't recognise strained to see past me, saying, *I heard a child crying*!

There's no child here, I told her.

I heard a child crying I cannot bear to hear a child crying, is it here? she babbled, head dodging right and left, poking forward like a chicken's.

No, I said, no child here.

She smiled, eyes trembling, neck taut. *I cannot bear it, I am a woman. I cannot bear to hear a child in pain. Perhaps it was a man I heard crying?* she asked slyly.

Perhaps a cat, I said.

Her long-nailed hand reached out but didn't touch me. We shrugged and she turned away.

I watched her tangled hair as she disappeared downstairs then I returned to my bed by the window. I looked down and after a few moments she emerged and crossed the street, entering the house opposite. I sipped the harsh red wine left over from breakfast, and gazed to my left where the street vanished into a haze of bars and intersections; then to my right, looking past the market, up and over until I could glimpse Sacre-Coeur white and wavering in the heat. When I look straight ahead, across the street into the window opposite my own, she was standing there staring at me. Then she turned away.

Though I lived there three more months, though I looked for her in the street, the market, the window, I never saw her again.

The Master

Robert Peett

ℭℬ

I know of a renegade priest who took to the mountains and hid himself away in a secret cave, there to meditate upon God and his own soul. He remained undisturbed by anything but existential doubts, mushrooms and an itch in the centre of his back for many years until by chance he was discovered by two poor peasants. They listened to his halting words (and scratched his back) as he unburdened himself of his lengthy meditations about how it is good to be good and lovely to love and be loved, and they were enraptured by the beauty and wisdom – they were particularly struck by the immanent niceness of the bits about re-distributing the God-given riches of the wealthy amongst the deserving poor. This seemed a penetrating and profound insight, a burning truth to shine like a… Well, anyway, they resolved that his message should be more widely heard and prevailed upon him to accompany them down the mountainside to their village of dessert-starved paupers.

These villagers, after some initial lack of interest, warmed to the priest and soon became disciples as firm and committed as the first two; before long they were marching on to the next village with the priest at their head. The caravan progressed through the land, slowing up all other traffic and swerving occasionally, and it was a matter of great sorrow when other priests and townspeople refused to listen. The sorrow came mostly from the true disciples, for the opponents of the Master of the Mountain (as the renegade priest had become known; it was embroidered on the back of his cloak by doting spinsters) generally did not live long enough to experience sorrow.

However, the Master was sickened by what he saw being done in his name for, although he had ideas he was no businessman, much less a marketing consulting or advertising executive and he could never have worked out the details of a fast-faith chain such as his disciples were doing. He begged to be allowed to stop this bloodily triumphal progress, but the servants could hardly allow their master to neglect his clear duty. Eventually the Master did escape (night, women's clothes, and a blind watchmaker who was on guard were all involved), and he went looking for a mountain.

The disciples at first thought to pursue him and persuade him of the error his ways. Then they realised that not only would the momentum of their crusade be lost, the Master was no longer strictly necessary. Oh the *message*, yes, yes – but the body? Wouldn't that be to raise him up in defiance of his own teaching? A kind of cult of the individual (no, that wasn't their term; they spoke a different language)? Rather as it isn't the individuals who become pope that matter but the office of the pope, the institution; thus it is an institution which has had entirely unimportant individuals in it. They did, however, need a figurehead and his name – or rather title – could not be jettisoned. But then they didn't want someone who might have thoughts or desires or will of any kind, so they looked around for a convenient corpse. They were spoilt for choice and finding one that resembled their erstwhile Master they dressed it in clothes like his and paraded him through the streets. Fortunately one of the disciples had learnt the arts used for Pope Formosus when his dead body was put on trial by Pope Stephen the Sixth and was a passable ventriloquist, thus enabling the Master to speak. Naturally they required a new corpse every few days to avoid their cause stinking to high heaven instead of aspiring to it. The ruse was never discovered, and most of the sect was slaughtered by followers of a renegade disciple (a former fisherman who became known as The Master of the Bait) a couple of years later.

As for the renegade priest and renegade master (one and the same, pay attention) he did indeed find another mountain but he had lost the knack of staying on it. One day he descended to a nearby village and, as luck would have it, his sect arrived soon after. Thus it came about that the dead body of the Master, incognito one might say since the disciples no longer recognised him, was used to imitate the live body of the Master. He was deeply unsatisfactory, for the appearance of the corpses, like facsimiles of facsimiles, remakes of remakes, had strayed further and further from the original and so he now did not look much like himself.

Sometimes Cary Grant Needs Defending

Carly Pluckrose

ᘓ

They say it's the little things. Little things you can't let go. The little habits and ticks that were once so cute but now frustrate and annoy. Little things that have grown too large to sweep under the carpet.

David likes to sing. Not in public (thank God) but when we're watching TV. He can't resist singing a line if a song title of lyric pops up on the news.

"Experts claim the results are not unusual..."

And off he goes. "...it's not unusual to be loved by anyone..."

Whilst I admit early on I may have encouraged such behaviour, three decades of marriage have dampened my appreciation somewhat, especially when he does it during the soaps.

"John please," begs a terribly wooden actress. *"Don't leave me this way."*

Cue David, "Don't, leave me, this waaaay," he sings, forever out of tune.

I let it go. Seemed like I'd been letting things go for years – the clicking of his tongue during meals, his assessment of the Dirty Dozen as *the* greatest movie ever, drunken dancing, his hatred of French cinema (and the French) – but we all have our breaking point. Mine was Cary Grant.

I was watching *An Affair to Remember* when David began insulting dear Cary. Now he knew full well Cary was my all-time favourite, but must have thought I'd just sit there in silent agreement as usual. But something inside me snapped. I jumped, as swiftly as my arthritis would allow, to my feet and screamed. The look on David's face was comical; he seemed genuinely scared. Maybe I shouldn't have used the staple gun or said those things about his sister (she probably does know the names of at least two of her children's fathers, if not their postcodes), but sometimes Cary Grant needs defending.

A Champion Returns

Mark Romasko

CR

It had just passed 3 o'clock, but in this corner of the snooker hall it could have been any time of day or night. What windows there were stood guard over the pool tables, the view outside providing a frame of reference for those who would stay for just one or two hours. Here, fifty paces, ten stairs and one heavy door away, there were no such distractions. The brass lights over the tables illuminated them in overlapping circles. The rest of the room was dimly lit, making everything else – players, tables, drinks alike – supporting actors to the baize.

John was snookered, and when John was snookered he didn't play in a hurry. He paced half around the table, and then back; leaned in, straightened up, coughed, scratched his neck, cleared his throat. A model of concentration.

I took a sip of my drink. Warm. Better finish it quickly and get another one. New notes from the cashpoint in my back pocket. "Done me up like a kipper," said John, to no-one in particular. I held my cue so that the tip blocked out a lamp near me, closing one eye to see the light feeding around it as though it were an eclipse in miniature.

I only had a tenner on this one. I'd wanted to go for twenty, but John wouldn't have it. In fact, I'd had a job getting him to accept the ten. The man wasn't short of a couple of bob, either; he'd passed round a picture of his BMW on his phone a while ago. Only one of those little ones, mind, but still. This had caused Aaron to start showing us his Honda Civic, gleaming in silver. He was a Honda man all over. It had been shot so you could see that his house was detached. "So we can't hear the neighbours. Well, more so they can't hear me!" He was in a band or something. Playing this Friday. Would I come? Maybe, I said, but I knew that it was too far away.

Aaron had been more keen on the reunion; apart from me, I mean, I was the one who organised it. John had needed some persuading. In the end he said he would come, but he'd have to go home by 10 so he could get a train. I told him that the Hurricane had died and we were doing it in his honour, but it made no difference. He said he had to work. Who works on a Sunday, double time or not?

I finished my pint, stood up and took some empties back to the bar. It was a habit I'd picked up working in a pub in Stepney, back in the seventies. If a man takes empties back to the bar off his own back he's worked in a pub before, odds on.

"Same again." Behind me came a murmur, then an "oh...", the type of noise that told me that John had missed, but not by much. When I got back with the tray he was placing the cue ball carefully behind the green, from where it had just come.

"Hey, Peter Ebdon," I said, "slow down a minute!" He hated being called that. "Come over here. A toast."

"To what?" John straightened, came toward me. "To us?"

"To the Hurricane, you plank. The greatest."

"Oh, right. Well, to the Hurricane!"

We clinked glasses, drank. John went back to the table and, after what seemed like a month, played again. It came off two cushions and rolled slowly into a group of reds. We cheered and clapped and slapped him on the back and the barman looked over at us with a small smile.

Evening was starting to draw in, but I only knew because I'd been for a walk. I had beaten John twice. Aaron I had beaten the first time, then the second had gone down to the wire. I would have won it but the black had gone in the jaws and come out again and then he had fluked a snooker he didn't even mean. I said I was going to get some fresh air but really I was pissed off and wanted to get out of there for a minute. It had been double or nothing as well so it was as good as forty quid.

When I came back Aaron must have just beaten John because the table was empty and he was strutting around a bit. I think the guy reckons he's Mick Jagger even though he was born in Bristol and fixed computers or something. Anyway we had a break to get some food and we began reminiscing. "Do you remember the night..." started John, and he is getting into it a bit, but he is telling it all wrong so I stop him and tell it myself and do it right.

It was 1982, the local championships. Usually there'd be twenty, thirty entrants, but people had all been watching the Hurricane, God rest his soul, and now any idiot with a cue thought that he could play snooker. So they had limited the number of players at sixty-four, and we had to start earlier to get all the games in. Now the first guy I had, he was useless. I finished him off five nil, and not once did he make more than thirty. Come the end, he looked distraught, so I didn't push it. But that was my first whitewash.

The second guy was a bit better. He was Irish as they come but he was a good lad. I beat him five one and he shook my hand and bought me a Guinness. Never seen him again. Third guy rocks up with this custom built cue and a red waistcoat with flowers on it. Stands there drinking a gin and tonic and whistling. Anyway I beat the guy five nil and tell him to get his pants down 'cause it's a whitewash. He won't and I offer him my hand and he walks away. First class prick.

Now I was into the last eight and, let me tell you, this guy was the worst of the lot. He was called John and he played like Peter Ebdon. You have never seen a slower, more doddery old player than this guy. I don't know what he's up to now – I guess it takes him an hour to put his pants on in the morning. Fair play to him, he did take a couple of frames off me.

Everything takes so long with this guy that it was getting late now, and in this place we don't drink water. It's the same for everyone – it's just what you do, isn't it? Well, I'd been watching the guy I had next and he'd been on the orange juice all day. Now to me, that's just cheating. Drinking's just a part of the game. But some people won't get into the spirit. I offered him a pint at the start of the round and he looked at me like I'd spat in his face and just shook his head. So I thought, right, you little toerag, you're going down.

Trouble is, he was quite good. He wasn't the best potter but he wouldn't leave you anything. He would snooker you and then just stand back with this big smirk on his face. After the first couple of frames he would start heckling in between shots, trying to needle. He got to four three up and came right up in my face and laughed. So I went away and got a break of eighty and kicked his arse in the next one, then I went and gave him some back. Said, "How do you like that?" But he just turned away.

Now it was the decider. No-one could take control of it. It must have been about thirty all. He was needling me but I didn't listen. Then he pulled off this great snooker, out of nowhere. Fair play to the guy, it was a great shot. He'd done me up like a kipper and I could see him looking pleased with himself, drinking orange juice in the corner.

I just shut my eyes and thought, what would the Hurricane do? Suddenly, it all looked so obvious. It was difficult, but if you played it exactly right... Anyway, I just went for it. I hit it and it came off three cushions and rolled into the reds. Now most of the pub was watching and they all started cheering. The other guy, he must have thought there was no way out from there, because his face looked like he'd just lost his house.

So I beat him quite easily from there and I go to shake his hand. "No way," he says, "you're a cheat." I pushed him and told him to take it back, but he said it again. So I punched him and as he was going down I hit him across the head with the cue. He was on the floor now so I picked up the white and threw it at him. Knocked his front teeth out and he lay there and people pulled me back. The barman nodded to the bouncer, who was this big black guy, and he just said, "Come with me." So I didn't have much choice. The man was huge! Deepest voice you ever heard.

So he leads me through this door and up some stairs and we're in some kind of office. I thought he was going to beat me up, that was that. He said, "You need to calm down. You drunk?" I said that I'd had a few but I wasn't drunk. He said, "You need to calm down. Me and the manager, we've both got money on you. So take it easy. You want some of this?" So he got some of the white stuff out of his pocket and cut up a couple of lines. "Take that." I had one and waited for him to have his. "Both for you, my friend. You need to win this for us. Go and do us proud." Then he smiled and he must have had about six gold teeth. Wonder how he got them? So I had the other one and went down.

When I came back the last guy was still there looking for trouble so the bouncer threw him out the door and gave him a couple to make sure he didn't come back. Some people are just stupid, you know? Anyway, from then on I was unstoppable. The guy who made the final was pretty good, O'Brien or something. Another Irish fellow. Played some proper competitive tournaments and everything. Didn't bother me though, I went two in front early on and started pulling off some outrageous shots. The crowd were loving it. In the end I won five two and the guy bought me a brandy and said, "You see this man? We've got the Hurricane and the Whirlwind... Well, this guy's the Typhoon!" And they gave me three cheers and everyone wanted to buy me a drink. I got two hundred and fifty for the prize pot, back when that was a lot of money. Cash in hand. I felt like I'd made it.

I don't know when I left but I decided to get a cab to London. We were going through the West End and I told the driver to take me to a casino. When we got there some guy tried to stop me as I was going in, so I showed him the money and he let me through. I went on the roulette for a bit and I was doing OK, breaking even. There was this girl by the bar and I bought her a few drinks and she came over to the table I was on.

I must have had about two hundred left at this point and I just thought I should go for broke. So I put it all on red and the guy span the wheel. Suddenly I thought of the bouncer in the snooker club and all I could see was this black face smiling with the gold teeth and I moved it onto black, but the guy must have said 'No more bets' because he wanted me to move it back. I said to him, "Come on, I'm an honourable man and this is my one chance." Something like that. It must have worked because he gave me a nod and left me alone.

It landed on black and I thought that I could kiss that bouncer if I saw him again. I just jumped around for a bit and the girl took my arm and said, "Come on, let's go." So I cashed in the winnings and she said, "We're going to the Ritz." We went to the Ritz and ordered up a lobster to the room at three in the morning. Next day I had enough left to go to the Ivy so I took her out I had *foie gras* and pheasant and I asked her to move in with me. She said yes and I felt like the happiest man alive. Six months later I asked her to marry me. Mrs Liza Robinson. Quite a ring to it, don't you think?

"So how is Liza?" said John.

"She's doing alright. Don't hear from her much. She's in Edinburgh now."

"Her kid just got into St Andrews?"

"Yeah, that's what I heard. Smart guy."

"Sarah just got into Nottingham. Says..."

I let Aaron pick up my side of the conversation and left them to it. Kids. Who needs them? Either they do well and make you feel inadequate, or they screw it up and everyone blames you. More trouble than they're worth.

John left soon afterwards. I played Aaron a couple of times and got twenty quid off him, then I got us both a whisky. He got a tenner back off me then said he had to go about half ten. I got him to stay for one more and won the tenner back and then he shook my hand and left.

I invited everyone else in the place to have a go and a couple of guys played for a frame and I beat them both pretty easily. Then no-one would challenge me so I just played by myself for a while, but I was getting a bit bored of it and when the barman called time I didn't hang around.

Maybe it was Aaron showing me his new BMW earlier that did it but when I saw my Golf parked in the drive it was as though I could make out every speck of rust, every bit of peeling paint. There was a little crack in the windscreen that I'd never got round to fixing. If it had been on the driver's side I would have got onto it right away. But it didn't bother me and no-one else had really complained. If they gave me a bonus this year I'd see whether I could get something a bit better. Something with a bit of class.

When I got home I made some cheese on toast and stuck a bit of chilli on top and opened up the Johnny Walker. All the lights were off in the other houses and it seemed far too quiet and to be honest it was making me a bit nervous. So I put the Pogues on the stereo and sang along a bit, but after a while the guy next door started banging on the wall so I turned it down a bit and stopped singing and poured myself another whisky.

I don't know why but I found myself standing in front of my trophy cabinet. Well, I call it a cabinet, but to be honest it's more of a shelf. There it was, my gold cup from the local championship in 1982, engraved Mark 'The Typhoon' Robinson... then the gold cups from 1983 and 1984. Next to that, a photo of me punching the air as I took a frame off Ray Reardon. It was the first round of the Masters and I'd get another two off him. Great times. A picture of Liza next to that, lying on a beach somewhere in Rhodes and toasting the camera with a cocktail. Then a silver for the local championships the next year, then... nothing. A few DVDs. I stood there for a while trying to think back but my mind wasn't playing along and kept drifting off somewhere else.

I got out the video of the Hurricane winning in '82 and put it in the VCR. It must have been a bit worn as the picture was crackly at the start and the sound changed pitch like a passing ambulance, but it soon sorted itself out.

I was having a few whiskies and getting into it and shouting out my support, then the neighbour started banging on the wall again so I banged back, but from that point I just clenched my fists and clapped to myself when the Hurricane pulled off a good shot. I got about half way through and then I must have fallen asleep because I didn't remember any more. The lights and the TV were on but at least I'd remembered to close the door. One out of three isn't bad. When I woke up my hand was still on the bottle of whisky and I felt like shit.

Next Stop, Squalor

Kerry Ryan

CS

I still think about Joan. When well-meaning people ask about the painting, I use what Stephen calls my professional voice and answer with a routine spiel about symbolism. Yet in my mind I am back there in the living room of Joan's tiny flat, with its yellowed anaglypta and second-hand teak, listening to Jack screech abuse while Joan snores quietly, her head tilted back on the old chair with its worn, brown upholstery. My nostrils fill with that familiar cabbage and chip pan smell of her home and I want to touch her neat grey hair, to stroke her soft, wrinkled cheek and wake her at last. But she sleeps on, just as she always did.

Destiny moves silently, or so they say. My move to Sarah's flat in the east of the city was fairly uneventful. My flatmates disappeared when it was time for me to leave and I was forced to lug all of my bags and boxes into the waiting taxi myself. But perhaps that was to be expected. We'd never been friends like Sarah and I were friends.

Supposedly I was doing Sarah and her boyfriend a favour by house-sitting while they were on a year-long tour of South America. Of course, Sarah was doing me the favour, allowing me to stay rent-free in a flat that made a mockery of the cramped bedsits I'd suffered since leaving home. Her property developer parents had paid for her trip and for the flat, situated in the kind of area estate agents describe as 'up and coming'. Still, it was a lovely flat and the truth is I was a little jealous – my parents preferred to spend their savings on Mediterranean cruises.

Sarah had befriended me during our first year at art school. I was never really sure why. I would have said we were close – as close as I was to anyone back then – yet in all those months of living in her flat, I received just one letter from her – no phone call, no email. She wrote in her mad looping hand of Chicomecoatl, snake women and other things I couldn't understand. It seemed they were still holed up in Mexico City, living on credit cards after spending all of her daddy's cash on Grade A cocaine. *We fly with Gods*, she wrote.

Years later I heard from someone that she was living on a wheat farm in the mid-West. Apparently, she'd become a hard-line Catholic after her husband (that same boyfriend?) ran away with another man.

That first night alone in Sarah's flat, I celebrated my isolation with two bottles of champagne I found chilling in the otherwise empty fridge. If I remember rightly, the hangover lasted longer than the excitement of living alone did. After a few days, it started to feel odd, not having anyone to talk to whenever I wanted, although in the old place I'd often prayed my flatmates would choke on that last stolen gulp of milk, that last stolen slice of bread.

Before moving into Sarah's place, I'd decided that sharing accommodation was to blame for my lack of creativity. If only I could be left alone without interruption then perhaps I could produce the kind of work which, in more optimistic moments, I still believed I was capable of. Although, there weren't many others who shared my optimism. In my final year at art school, a tutor I desperately wanted to please said to me quite matter-of-factly, *Your work to date has been a series of empty gestures.* I didn't cry then or later when I was alone. In those days I viewed tears as a sign of weakness.

Now the critics call that undergrad juvenilia my 'early minimalist period', and some of those canvases change hands for eye-boggling sums considering that the tutor's assessment wasn't so far off the mark. For years I'd found comfort in the stricture of the straight line, in the rationality of the right angle, the perfectly executed circle. I'd got stuck repeating the same old rubbish. I wanted to move on, to create something else, something different, but I didn't know where to start or what to do. So I set up my easel in the corner of Sarah's living room and waited for the magic to happen. Of course I couldn't even sketch out a simple little box—those little boxes I once loved. Instead, I spent my time sitting on the wooden chair by the bay window, watching the people come and go in the street below.

The scents from that street still wake me sometimes. Aromatic curry spice drifted out of kitchen windows to mingle with the smell of melting road tar in what lazy little slipstreams of breeze the weather granted. It was that second summer when the UK really started to boil: Scotland's first ever hose pipe ban, record beating sales of Irn Bru before the water ration cards were issued and the police stood guard at standpipes.

Once I witnessed a fight break out between locals and an English couple who were trying to smuggle barrels of water into a van. How they'd planned to get the barrels across border control I don't know, but before they could someone called the police. A tight group of neighbours blocked the van's exit, shouting racist abuse—some of the flats had posters in the window proclaiming: NO TO ENGLISH WATER RELIEF. When a big gorilla wearing nothing but the tiniest shorts and terrible sunburn punched the English man, the police waded in with tasers.

Normally though, nothing nearly as dramatic happened. It was just too hot. Bikini-clad girls and bare-chested boys, crazy with the temperature and tonic wine, kissed and argued sloppily, lazily on the close stoop, while dogs, too hot to sniff or shag, panted under the shadow of souped-up Fords. When the sun got too much, everyone went inside to their cool homes, to their own lives, and the shouts of a few lunatics too drunk to hide from the heat would be all that punctured the afternoon hush. I'd sit and watch from the window as afternoon became evening. African birds flapped in loose formation across the clay-tiled tenement rooftops while the sun as red as mars sank down from an alien sky streaked with purple and orange wisps of cloud.

Unable to sleep, I spent my nights hunched over the screen, buying things I didn't need or really want. Sometimes if I was feeling low enough, I'd type in the names of people I'd been at art school with, torturing myself with their news of shows, tours, commissions. Sometimes when the heat and the self-loathing got too much, I'd rest my sweating body against the cool livingroom wall; the incessant reggae bass from the flat downstairs causing the sandstone to vibrate ever so slightly against my cheek. It fascinated me, that ancient red boreal stone, full of silica and quartz, hewn from a Deeside quarry and saturated with thousands of years of existence. I would stand there for who-knew-how-long, my face pressed against the cold stone, listening, waiting for something, what I don't know; perhaps for the tiny grains to reveal their closely-guarded secrets.

Days and nights slowly passed without me speaking to another person face-to-face. Isn't it funny that now I wish I'd enjoyed the solitude when I had it? These days I'm surrounded by people – grandchildren, friends, friends of friends – who always want or need something and, of course, when I'm painting there is always someone there, watching, staring back at me from the canvas. Peace, silence, solitude was what house-sitting was supposed to provide, yet I frittered that precious time away worrying, pacing the varnished floorboards and trying to avoid the stare of the blank canvas in the corner.

The night I first heard Jack go off at Joan, I'd managed a rare sleep on the sofa. Just a few days before, I'd met the new upstairs neighbour on the stairwell and we'd exchanged a nod. She was a poor old sort but seemed harmless enough, a little doddering if anything, so I never quite expected to hear that level of noise coming down through the ceiling.

Shocked awake and half mad from lack of sleep, I staggered upstairs, knocking gently at first before hammering, beating the wood. To my surprise, the door swung open. The lock was faulty no doubt because it had been kicked in so many times. It was that kind of street back then, not the palm tree-lined executive address chock-a-block with SUVs and soft-tops it has become.

It may sound like an exaggeration when I say I felt *compelled* to walk into Joan's flat. I don't know why. Nosiness, Stephen said, but I like to think it was more than that. Perhaps it was need.

In the small living room, Jack was perched in his corner, stamping around and screaming obscenities in a Glaswegian accent. Joan slept on in her old, brown armchair, a sheen of sweat across her slack face and her white vest damp down the front. It was clear what was going on: a squawking attention-seeker with a sailor's mouth and a tired old woman who'd drank too much. There was a half empty bottle of gin by the side of her chair and her hand held a glass drained of everything bar the lemon.

The room looked tired and washed out – the heavy teak furniture and ugly vinyl prints gave it the air of a dilapidated seaside B&B. Yet there was something about it. Something in this little scene that said so much. It was as though I'd stumbled in on the denouement of a one-act tragedy.

Gently I went over to the chair and tried to wake Joan but she was out cold. Jack, oblivious to my presence, continued with his swearing – something I was to become wearily familiar with as the weeks and months progressed. Later I would guess Joan's military background had helped him develop such a range of international swear words. For from the few photographs and medals on top of the sideboard, I gathered she'd been in the army. There was a photograph of a much younger, healthier Joan linking arms with another woman in uniform somewhere that looked African: all blue skies and arid land. Beside this was a black-and-white photograph of a small girl in a starched dress standing outside the

Co-op on the main road. The shop front hadn't changed all that much, although Joan certainly had. There were no photographs of anybody else – children or adults – but pinned on a square of felt behind a glass frame were two medals awarded by WRAC, one for long service and I don't know what the other was for. Anyway, that was how I discovered her name was Joan Dean.

That first night I didn't do much looking around. I was too busy trying to calm Jack down and trying to wake Joan up. Realising it was hopeless, I went back downstairs and put some music on to drown him out. I promised myself I would complain first thing the next day, but the sadness of that little room, Joan's gaping toothless mouth and Jack's messy corner prevented me. And anyway, he'd shouted himself silent by midnight so I didn't really see the point.

During the weeks that followed, I made an effort to say hello to Joan on the stairwell or outside the shop. Small talk seemed enough then. I never did manage to ask her when she'd lived around there or why she had come back. There was a lot I never asked and some things I never told. I never mentioned those weekly visits upstairs. It just didn't seem right somehow to embarrass her like that.

But alone in Sarah's flat, I came to anticipate my Thursday visits upstairs. Perhaps even look forward to them. Joan would get her pension, drink too much, and Jack would make a protest at her passing out before him. As quietly as I could, I'd push open her front door, go in and hush Jack with something I'd found in the fridge or the cupboard. At first I brought biscuits or a bit of cake until he demanded whisky. He'd developed quite a taste for it over the years. The old soak.

One week I went upstairs to find that Joan had fallen asleep with her glasses on and so slowly I took them off, placing them on the table beside her, ready for when she woke up. I didn't mind doing these little things. I liked to think I was helping. Or so I told myself. Now I know Joan was actually helping me.

Stephen thinks I exaggerate when I say that without her my life would never have taken the route it did. But really it's only too true. That tableau of Joan and Jack, the symmetry of it, the sadness, the stark poverty, something about it haunted me. Wherever I was – walking in the park, microwaving my dinner, watching the riots on the news – that Thursday night scene would come to mind and something sore would rise up. *Old age is such a terrible shipwreck* – I didn't know who said it or when but during my time at Sarah's that sentence rattled and rattled around my head.

Then it happened. Whatever had been snarling up inside me for so long was loosed. Yet despite how consumed, how eager I was, it still took me weeks to get Joan's face right. I did it over and over again until the canvas was thick with paint and I had to scrape it all off and start again. I worked day and night, existing on coffee and a little take-out food I'd pick at whenever I remembered. I hardly washed. I hardly slept. I thought about nothing else except *getting it right*.

Each week the anticipation of going upstairs became almost too much. Sometimes I would be tempted to walk up there before Thursday but, of course, I couldn't risk having to explain myself. So I waited.

I don't know whether it was painting the intricate lines that made up Joan's crumpled face or the congealed meal-for-one in front of her that I realised I had to get away from that flat before I too was marooned. Age was the only real difference between us, and at least Joan had Jack, all I had was my heart beating morbidly in my chest. So I asked my parents for one last loan and I was able to move to the artists' colony and what happened, happened.

I'll be honest, I didn't really think about Joan much after I moved away. I was working, creating and that was all that seemed to matter then. If I had known that that private Thursday night scene would become such a public spectacle, I would've returned and if she had moved, I would have found her. I would have. I could have paid her a fee for all the times she sat for me without realising it. Now, I know, it's too late.

Everywhere I travel, I see her. In art stores and gallery shops across the globe, there she is sleeping on mugs, notebooks, bookmarks – even napkins for God's sake – with Jack on his perch behind her chair, yelling obscenities that only I can hear.

I still can't get out of the habit, after all these years, of calling Jack a he, but I suppose I should really say she. It wasn't until years later, when I read a coffee table tome on the New Glasgow Realists that I was informed that I'd actually painted a female parrot rather than a male. The males are green, apparently. I suppose I just took it for granted that something that caused so much fuss had to be male.

Of course, now parrots are commonplace on Glasgow's streets and squares – they outnumber the pigeons. When I see the hot pink, powder blue and sun-bright yellow of a thousand wings beating wildly in the air above George Square, I wonder if I should have flung that cage door wide open and allowed Jack to fly away over the rooftops. I wonder if she would have left when she had the chance.

The Bowler Hat

Beryl Sabel

ଔ

I have two photographs of my great-grandfather. Both show a small thin man wearing a bowler hat. Now immigrant Jews living in the East End of London at the beginning of the 20th century did not wear bowler hats. And this was not the only unusual thing about Moshe Kablovsky. Whereas the vast majority of his fellow Jews worked in the rag trade Moshe was a carpenter, and no mere banger-in of nails at that but a self-employed master craftsman.

As a small girl I would go into my grandparent's bedroom to run my fingers over the satin-smooth surface of the beautiful mahogany head-and-foot-boards Moshe had made as a wedding present for his daughter. I don't know what happened to the bed when they died. Today it would probably be worth a small fortune.

Still I did inherit something he had made: a pair of picture-frames. Against a background of some very dark dull wood he created delicate geometric patterns in a lighter golden wood that shine like star-bursts. They are exquisite and I cherish them.

But back to the hat. When he arrived in this country Moshe spoke not a word of English and was penniless and friendless. The ship he'd boarded in Odessa was supposed to be going to America where he had cousins who were willing to take him in. Distant cousins admittedly, but family is family. This situation was only too common and the established Jewish community in Britain did what it could to help. The Jews' Temporary Shelter in Leman Street was the salvation of many immigrants. The area, known as St Georges in the East, was convenient for the docks. Every ship was met as it docked and the immigrants were provided with bed and board for up to fourteen days while they made arrangements for their future. The thinking behind this charity was no doubt partly self-serving. Anglo-Jews didn't want penniless immigrants with outlandish ways to sully the image they themselves had cultivated over the years: Englishmen who happened to be Jews. Whatever the motive, the Shelter was a lifesaver for thousands of Jews during the great exodus from Russia.

As it was for Moshe Kablovsky. It was here, while being kitted out from the Shelter's store of second-hand clothing, that he found and claimed the bowler hat. Who knows why? Perhaps he needed something to help him establish his identity, his sense of self. Perhaps it simply appealed to the clown in him – he loved to play the fool, my grandmother said. Whatever the reason, Moshe walked the streets of the East End wearing his bowler hat. This, of course, made him distinctive.

Now the East End at that time was not without its anti-Semitism, though compared to the pogroms in Russia from which the Jews had fled it was a mere flea-bite. And it had yet to reach the extremes it did in the 1930's with the Moselyites. But it did exist. People felt their livelihoods threatened by immigrants willing to work for low wages in appalling conditions. Indeed, things are not much different today over a hundred years later, though the immigrants are no longer Jews. Anyway, the abuse was mainly verbal, with the occasional brawl.

The bowler hat made it almost inevitable that Moshe would be subjected to abuse. One day a small group of youths began to shout obscenities at him as he walked along Whitechapel Road on his way home from work. He ignored them. Frustrated at not getting a reaction from him they soon decided to go for something a bit more physical. So one day they waited until he turned into a quieter road, then jumped him and began pounding him with their fists. As he was so short, most of the blows landed on his head which was quite well protected by the bowler hat.

Three days of this and Moshe had had enough. The next day the assault was over almost before it began. Before leaving his workshop that afternoon Moshe had knocked some nails into a small piece of wood so that they projected by about an inch. He had then placed the piece of wood on his head, nails pointing upward, and jammed his hat over the wood. No further attacks occurred and though there were now several small holes in the hat they evidently didn't bother Moshe because a few days later he went and had his photograph taken – wearing the bowler hat. In the photo you can't actually see the holes but I don't suppose Moshe cared. He knew they were there.

I call them his 'before' and 'after' pictures and they have pride of place on my living room wall, in the frames he himself made, testament to a small but indomitable man.

Skin & Guts

Marc R Sherland

ॐ

He learned to shoot when a nipper, his father taking him to the misty moors behind their ramshackle terrace slum and getting him to take pot shots at unwary rabbits in the glistening moonlight. Every shot needed to count, as ammunition was expensive, so for every rabbit which missed its place in the pot, Freddie got a weal across his bare legs, stung with his father's army belt. It taught him to be an excellent shot. He was also expected to skin and gut the catch without sentiment or qualm.

His dad died when Freddie was twelve years old. Tuberculosis took hold in lungs festered by war gassing, within two years, the man was dead. Good riddance to him.

Freddie went to school when work and chores allowed him, but learning did not stick to his ribs like a good rabbit stew. The teacher Mr. Philip, stood in front of class and tapping the rule on his desk would get them to recite the 'times tables'.

"5 times 1 is 5,

5 times 2 is 10,

5 times 3 is 15,

5 times 4 is …."

Freddie understood the rhythm, recognised the words, but could never get the sense of them.

Old teach, would glance over his horn rim glasses and watch the mumbling words fall from childish lips, like the drone of incessant bees, knowing that no pollen was being collected. Except for those seated at the top right hand corner of the room, there was no honey to be made here, and even they, would likely end in an elementary school, rather than gain a grammar school scholarship.

At the end of the day he would announce "You boys are nothing but cannon fodder, except for you Frederick Horne, you are destined to be a poacher, or sniper."

Freddie had brothers and sisters to help feed, for his mother had to work at two jobs just to make ends meet. By day she took in washing and by evening she worked as an usher in the Regal cinema, collecting lost handkerchiefs left at the 'weepies', washing them and selling them at weekends at the market, along with other 'found' trinkets.

From the age of ten, Freddie made his way by filling sacks with coal, perched on the back of a wooden truck, which trundled along half baked roads, horse hooves attempting to avoid laming potholes every few yards. His regular customers knew him for his trademark whistling, as he bore heavy sacks on his back to the bunkers outside the slum doors. Many a time he had to turn heel still borne down with the weight, as a regular had no money to pay for fuel and no credit worth the interest.

Sometimes he would see some smirking tike playing in the gutter and he would challenge them to carry the half hundred weight of coal up to the door. He would laugh as boys twice his size couldn't manage what he had learned the knack to hoist. For all the bone crunching labour, Freddie grew strong and broad shouldered. He would have made a reasonable catch for one of the local lasses, but war interjected.

One day at the evening meal, the one family gathering time, conversation dwelt on that subject, with the younger boys moaning that they were too young to join the forces and Freddie wondering which service he should join.

Naomi his thirteen year old sister said "I'm gonna be a nirse, an sew up all their bullit hols."

Freddie quipped, "Well they'll all die av gangereen from yer awful stitchin and th muck on yer grey mitts."

She slammed down her knife and hid her hands behind her back. Washing water was available once a day, last thing at night, for it had to be fetched from the pump in the street.

"Yer a bustard," she replied, "At least I don't haulk coal all day for a livin."

He made a grim smile, annoyed at the slight but secretly pleased that she wanted to do her bit.

He discovered that the dockyard needed labourers and having built muscles with the coal, reckoned that at sixteen he had the qualifications to fit the job. He was right, he was taken on at first sight and employed moving lumps of metal and wood and hammering and shoving them around. Foremen admired him, for his ready willingness to do a job and get on with it, never complaining at even the toughest request. He got any overtime that was going and he took it no matter how many hours he had already worked in a week. War made slaves of labourers, in all but wages, and he was tethered to the war effort.

In 1944 the HMS Bulldog was docked at the shipyard, due to undergo some minor repairs, whilst being loaded with a cargo of explosives and shells due for the continent.

The Luftwaffe had been sending bombs across the channel to drop on industry, but so far the shipyard had escaped.

By moonlight urgent loading continued. One private tried to hoist ordnance too heavy and awkward. Freddie who was working late got a call to go help, his knack had been noticed. Before he could board the ship the private dropped the case of shells and they exploded setting off a chain reaction of terrible thuds and blasts until the whole ship was ablaze with firecracker whizzes and bangs. Less than a minute, one almighty explosion began to break up the stricken vessel. The crew who had been confined to ship spilled over the side of the sinking boat, but they fell into an inferno of chemical enriched flames as munitions and diesel combined to light the water.

The Dockyard Police Commander, was his old teacher who had been re-enlisted. Desmond Philip took seconds to asses the situation. The men in the water were screaming to be saved. They were soaked in diesel and scorched by chemicals, wailing for mothers and praying to god to save them.

"Horne", he said. "I've got to ask you to do a terrible thing. There is no way to save these men, but we can help them."

Freddie stood on the edge of the dock with a rifle and shot the burning and dying men, just like shooting rabbits in the moonlight.

Theft

Kathrine Sowerby

ଔ

Light spilled onto the floor giving Roslyn time to memorise the positions of the slugs before the fridge door swung shut; a trick she'd learnt on her nightly trips to heat milk for the baby. Salt on the skirting boards didn't work and too often she'd felt the squish of a bulbous body between her toes, so she stepped carefully across the room to the sink. As she filled a glass the breeze from the open window blew over her hand. All the windows downstairs were painted shut, always had been, but now pine needles dangled in disturbed cobwebs from the splintered frame. And her purse, left by the cooker to dole out dinner money in the morning, was gone.

Her boots were in the porch. She stepped into them and pulled the door behind her. Out of the garden she followed the hedge that bordered the house onto the path that led up to the school. She stopped to listen for sounds in the bushes. There was only the distant clanking of work on the railway tracks. She shivered, drew her cardigan round her chest and crossed her arms. Something bigger than a fox moved on the hill.

Roslyn's breath grew heavier as she reached the top. Lights sparkled across the city. The fence round the school was high and the path overgrown but she could see, sitting on a low brick wall by the school's entrance, a man rummaging in his lap. She watched him toss receipts, used train tickets and library cards to one side. Passport photos of her children. She took a step and heard a crack. The man looked round. He threw the purse in the bushes and ran. Roslyn lifted her boot. Shards of shell pierced the snail's flesh, releasing its iridescent slime.

Please, Sir!

Charlie Taylor

ငွ

Jerry 'Juicy' Jewison looked forward to history lessons. They were on a par with bunking off to town every Wednesday afternoon, thumping Kenny Tunstall in the kidneys, shoplifting from Woolies on the way home, and masturbation contests in the school's old air raid shelters.

Juicy finished cutting Brian Povey's cap into four pieces and deposited the tattered remains on the table standing at the front of the rows of old wooden desks, all set on iron frames, with inkwells no longer used in this just-post-war age of the Bic and the Biro.

"He's coming!" hissed the lookout at the door.

Juicy and his pals began a slow, rhythmical banging of their desk lids, the pace increasing until the classroom door was flung open. An insolent silence greeted the tortured presence of Mr Stott, human stick insect, all billowing black gown, horn-rimmed spectacles, jerky movements and hysteria.

"Stop that damn noise at once!" he shrieked.

Juicy twanged a wooden ruler against the underside of his desk: boinnnnggggg! Mr Stott's head twitched in his general direction. Rammy Ramsdale twanged a ruler on the other side of the room and Mr Stott's head twitched the other way. Minger Morris twanged in turn from his desk by the window and as the head turned this way then that way, Ned Cartwright fired a paper pellet from a sturdy rubber band stretched between thumb and forefinger. It stung Old Stotty below the left ear. The class erupted.

It came as a surprise to Juicy to learn, after the trial, that Old Stotty had been blown up in a tank in the First World War. "That's still no excuse for beating young Ned up," said his dad after the trial. "The man deserved all he got."

Juicy smiled and thought of Kenny Tunstall.

The Scarlet Heart

Lynne Voyce

ભ

Alice Clisswell lost her heart
He threw it in the donkey cart.
Kick the barrel
With boots of Spanish leather
Brought seven hundred miles
Over land and sea
Dangling around his neck
As he walked up the lane
And set eyes on me.
My vagabond lover.
My heart.
Gone.
Kick it until it topples.
There.
There it goes.
Our father, who art in heaven ...
God forgive me for I have sinned.
I have lost myself.
I am scarlet.

Mariah makes the bed with the precision of a bored and disappointed woman: if she is slapdash the painstaking structures of her life will collapse. The glint of her wedding ring in the dim static bedroom, as she smoothes the eiderdown, reminds her of this: it is heavy on her finger. If only last week's letter hadn't hinted at escape.

She looks out of the window, through the November twilight to the village green. Genteel in the warmer months, now a dark little island; at its centre the Scarlet Oak, born not long after Christ himself: trunk a black hollow, naked winter crown scratching the black-eye sky. Her home, Scarlet Cottage, is named after it. Two girls eke the last minutes from the day; breath a stream of laughter, ponytails flying, careless feet lodged in a makeshift noose.

Harold strides down the pavement; everything moving at speed, but for his brief case: ballast to body and mind.

Uninterested, she watches the girls get off their swing, stagger, giggle, pull the rope down and drag it to the red door across the green.

"I'm home!" His sensible footfalls are on the crooked stairs. "Darling!" He stands at the bedroom door while the cat, Mab – having appeared from nowhere – circles his ankles like a length of black rope. "I've a great idea: a documentary on Scarlet Cottage."

"Our own home? A bit cheap, don't you think?" She loves the house, the very bricks, beams and clay of the place. She felt an affinity with the building the moment she walked in. Biting her tongue she straightens the curtains and glances back out of the window. At first she sees nothing, her eyes unable to readjust but then there is a flash of red. A kite? An anoraked child? Wind blown trash?

Cupping her hands, she presses her face to the cold glass – gasps. A young woman is hanging from a branch of the Scarlet Oak like a swinging pendulum. Mariah can see every detail in the evening grey: vibrant auburn hair, full-skirted red taffeta dress, white petticoat hem, laced eyelets of the delicate ebony boots. The girl's indigo eyes wide open look straight at her from an impossibly pale face, marked with vein blue lips. Dead.

"Jesus Christ." She turns. Harold isn't there. She turns back, sick with panic, but the girl is gone.

Mariah runs her finger over the flamboyant signature and dreams of him: Vincent.

"Can we meet?" he has written.

Life with Vincent would have been very different. She places the letter in the bureau, next to her passport. She hasn't used the latter for years. Harold won't go on holiday in case he misses an opportunity at work. Mariah dreams of travel: Valley of the Kings, Golden Temple, Ayres Rock; wearing crisp white linen and straw panama. She often imagines herself different: dancing in high-heels, hair loose, an orchid at her ear; or the raconteur, waving an expressive Gitane. But mostly she pictures herself with children

"Kids tie you down," Harold often says, his voice softly domineering, "I'm ambitious darling. Let's wait eh?" They've lived here nine years and she's still waiting.

"I saw you looking at this in Grey's, happy anniversary."

Harold hands Mariah a narrow box, runs his hand over Mab; inside a necklace of fire opals flickers in the hearth light. He takes it, puts it round her neck, his breath on her cheek: "You look lovely."

They turn towards the black window, study their reflection. Momentarily she thinks she sees the hanging girl, delineated by the headlamps of a passing car but it is just a trick of the light. "Thank you Harold." She shrugs free then heads upstairs to put on red silk, black velvet and to find a way to keep trying.

The new moon is a slip of silver in the sky and Harold isn't home. He rarely is.

"Research," he had said. Mariah marvels at the necklace's ever-changing stones as she catches sight of her reflection. She had looked at it in the window of Greys for just a moment. Harold had noticed. But he hasn't noticed her boredom, something far more apparent.

There is the singular sound of an owl outside. It agitates the cat. She hears Nana Tilda's half forgotten, boreal voice – "the hoot of an owl bodes ill" – shivers.

Mariah is superstitious. Childhood voices are hard to silence. She grew up not far from here with her grandmother. She was an only child in a lonely row of railway cottages, her sole company a rattling train every seven minutes past the hour. The neighbours, superstitious old women, prematurely widowed to Capstan Full Strength and blue-collar work, took pleasure in frightening her. "Break your egg shell," they'd whisper, "it lets the devil out"; "don't pass on the stairs"; "don't break mirrors"; "don't put new shoes on the table". Every day infused with the fear of ill luck. If ever she has children she won't fill their heads with such nonsense, if ever.

To cheer her self, she goes to the bureau, takes out the letter, re-reads it. This is her chance to escape. She takes a slice of paper: "Dear Vincent…" But as the words form there is a flicker outside. Red. Please not again. Drawn by dreadful curiosity, she goes to the window. It is the girl, swinging in the evening drizzle: hair matted, booted feet twitching, lips blue, eyes a luminous void.

"No! No, go away!" Mariah closes her eyes, uses the only means of spiritual protection she knows: "Our father who art in heaven…" There is a moment of weird perception, a collage of owls, cats, the girl's dead face. "Amen." Her eyes open. Is the spell broken? The girl has gone but the sense of foreboding has not.

Harold arrives home, wearing a sodden, satisfied grin: "I found the grave of a girl, at the far end of the churchyard. It used to be unconsecrated." He unbuttons his coat. "Alice Clisswell. She lived in this house all her life. First with her mother, then her husband. Committed suicide when she was nineteen." Harold doesn't notice his wife's ghostly expression; doesn't notice her crumple into the chair trembling. Instead he sucks his teeth at Mab, pats his lap. "Hung herself," he says simply. "They keep the suicide note in the church. Adultery with some drifter while her husband was at Trafalgar. The bloke moved on. Broke her heart. Of course there was the guilt, the scandal. It's got prime time BBC2 written all over it."

But all Mariah can hear is the intermittent hoot of an owl, far away.

Mariah drinks coffee while Harold ignores her. She breathes in home: cat in the inglenook, the flood of morning sun, the smell of slowly wilting anniversary flowers, (odd to smell spring in the midst of winter).

She has a half memory of when they viewed the house. There had been flowers then: jars of sweet peas, freesias, pansies, along the windowsills, on the tables. She had fallen in love with the place. Mrs Petit stood by the fireplace, round hipped, kids hanging from her like tree decorations, eyes and hair wired with divorce: "The children love flowers, they make perfume from petals. There won't be many flowers where we're going."

Mariah didn't understand Mrs Petit's sorrow at the time. The woman had all that Mariah wanted: insistent, persistent, inconvenient love of children.

"Do you want children Harold?" Mariah had asked walking back from the Odeon some ten years before.

"Of course."

They'd known each other six months. Vincent had gone to 'find himself' and she couldn't bare the loneliness, a symptom of the endless days alone with Grandma.

"When?" she'd asked, as she turned her newly acquired engagement ring so it resembled a wedding band.

"When the time's right."

It never has been. Was the longing for children that day with Mrs Petit the reason why now she can't quite remember what was said? Mrs Petit had mentioned the girl. Maybe. Yes, Mariah was sure.

A raven crashes against the small casement window, startles her; brings her back to the present. It tumbles then limps off across the oyster sky.

"Bloody hell, that was weird," says Harold as he kneels on the hearth and constructs a fire, "Oh, I'm meeting Bill, this afternoon. We're scouting locations for the background stuff."

"Would that include the pub?"

"Possibly."

"I'll stay here. Talk to the walls shall I?"

"Don't you want me to go?"

"I'm alone a lot, that's all…"

"I thought that friend was coming." He prods the coals.

"I couldn't face the children running about."

"Oh." He says nothing else. The mention of children always silences him. He puts the poker down and goes upstairs.

Mariah goes to an ancient lime washed wall, places her two hands flat against it. In the fabric of the house she finds the comfort she never finds from Harold.

It is easier to reply to Vincent than not she thinks as she stares at the blank paper; easier to find a split edge to breath through, than to unfold the whole thing with Harold and try again. In the morning she will pack her bags and go.

The fire blazes, Mab lies on the hearth, her machine gun purr melting into the soporiphic air. Outside the rain clatters on the windows, the wind howls through the thatch and a sulphurous flash floods the house, followed, twenty counts later, by a barely audible crack of thunder.

"Dear Vincent." The storm builds; she turns the mirror on top of the desk, so as not to let the devil in, and continues, "I think of you often." The weather pulls at the lead casements, rattles them furiously. "I will..." One of the window latches breaks free: the leaded pane bangs violently in its frame. Mab gets up startled, dashes towards the stairs.

Unconcerned by what she might see Mariah stands and goes to the window, consumed by the sad, thrill of replying. She'd summoned the girl in the red dress herself, linked her imminent adultery to something she'd heard years ago. But as she looks through the window, the girl is there, tossed by the deluge. Through the dark their eyes meet. And Mariah understands.

Turning, not caring from where the image has sprung, just knowing she has to rid herself of it, she snatches up Vincent's letter, snatches up her reply. The storm pelts the house as if it will sweep it away. She screws up the bruised papers, ink bleeding onto her fingers. The lights flicker and fail. The teeming rain is white noise. "Our father," she begins for the second time in a week and throws the letters on the flames. They leap in ecstasy while the papers twist and curl in a last dance.

"Amen," Mariah whispers.

She sinks to the floor, presses her cheek to the cold stone flags of the hearth. "I'll stay," she whispers, "I'll stay and try again." After what seems like minutes, she pushes herself up, returns to the rain-splashed window. The girl is gone; the rain has slowed; the wind passes over.

Picnic Weather

Mark Wagstaff

C3

I do things I never did when the children were little. When their mother and I split up or I left her or abandoned her, however she likes to play it they were nursery-schoolers and babies, bewildered at every visit, distraught at every goodbye. I was very much the wicked man who didn't care for his children and when you've a name that bad, you live up to it.

All archaeology now. We long since stopped talking about it because the reasons we got together and the reasons we split apart have all long since gone away. The children are nearly grown. Sally left school this summer; Terry and Stevie won't be far behind. Stevie wants to leave early, says he'd rather work. He was always a sharp lad. Terry's the one for exams. I can see him doing something brainy and lucrative. Hope he remembers his poor old dad.

I do things now I never did, like picnics. A wicked man, I could never stand all that football in the park. Always too keen to rush away to whatever was keeping me busy. But now the boys are allowed an occasional shandy and I'm not expected to bring anything but my wallet, I'm much more gracious. Marina always got somewhat tense when she called about trifling details of missing maintenance payments or to twist the scalpel about sleepless nights with their torn ligaments and fevers. That sunny morning, though, she sounded like ten hours' rest and a tax rebate. Picnic weather, she told me. We're celebrating Sally. I had some vague arrangement involving beer but rather than say I was busy – as I would in years gone by – I said yes. It wouldn't be a family picnic: it hadn't been my family in a long time.

Marina's peculiar strength is meticulous rage. When I was the bogeyman she hated me with the malice of Greek legend. When the children went to that overpriced school for their overcooked education there was no pencil case or tie-pin she didn't invoice to my name. The credit card oiks never grasped her poetic, restless revenge. Marina's idea of picnics had the same diligence. By the time I emptied her four-by-four of the trestle, the chairs, the basket and plates; options for carnivores, vegans and Sally; the desserts, the fruit and golf umbrella, it was minutes before I realised something was missing. Tom. "How's Tom?" I asked, the friendly way of uncaring ex-husbands.

She never paused setting out the glasses. "Red or white?"

She invited her brother and his weird wife, and I enjoyed watching their kiddies run them ragged. Marina's Uncle Dan pitched up so we went for a manly smoke down by the river, while virtuous ex-brother-in-law scraped plates. Dan's a strange old man so we always kept in touch. He told me it was: "Good riddance."

"Where did Tom go?"

Dan chuckled. "Some motel where he gets discount."

My surprise that my bland replacement could do anything so tasty was wholly genuine. I couldn't help laughing.

"He was long enough about it," said Dan.

It was picnic weather. The unforgiving sun drove our pale scalps into the shade of the willows. Under that curtain of lacy green we found Sally hunkered with her chin on her knees.

"Think I heard a bottle open." Dan twinkled away, wisest of strange uncles.

Not entirely comfortably, I sat next to my daughter. Sally's not like her mother, not like me. She's maybe a touch of her aunt, my kid sister, who no one remembers now except as a jar of rusty ashes. Sally stared into the willow leaves in that same tense, impending way of teenage women, that frozen-fire way we grow up to forget. With only worldly things to clutch at, I fidgeted on the hard ground. I lit a cigarette.

"Don't offer then."

I should have said: does your mum know? But I didn't. "I heard about Tom." I wondered why she should care what I heard.

"Yeah."

As the eldest, her eyes always found me wanting at each muttered see-you-later as I pressed some stupid, large sum of money into her baby hands. "He was with your mum a long time."

"Longer than you." She blew smoke at the trees.

I couldn't even ask: how's school? At eighteen it no longer wanted her. "Doing anything nice the summer?"

"No." She half-hid her face in the crook of her arm. "I got to do forms."

"Forms?" Always troublesome. And costly.

"University. Straight As if you remember."

"Everyone gets As."

"Piss off." She flicked her cigarette butt at an anthill. A few rushed out, darting kamikaze to the big heat. "I got in Oxford. Law. Good college. Good prospects."

I'm not so stupid to congratulate people. "Prospects of what?"

"Income, dad. Employment. Those things you're too busy for."

"How's the painting?"

"You don't care about painting."

"I asked didn't I?"

"Yeah, like I asked Tom why he was going. Like I asked you."

I gave her another smoke, as lethal a gift as my gene pool.

"I've had another offer." She dragged out the words unwillingly. "London. Fine art. She doesn't know. No one knows I applied."

"It's good to have options."

"Yeah, your life's one bloody big option isn't it? She's already met my tutors. Bought the books. She's told everyone: My daughter's at Oxford."

"What about London?"

"Are you deaf or just thick? Everyone knows I'm going to Oxford."

I used to hold her and lie how everything was for the best. "So take London. Screw Oxford."

"It's so easy for you isn't it? You just don't care what happens."

I stood, cramp walking me like an old man. Not a sly uncle: like my old man who never got what he wanted in life and never let me forget it. "We can go to London. It's easy. There's plenty of places to stay." I closed my eyes, not caring what happened.

Drinking with Dionysus

Simon Wroe

ℭℨ

First thoughts. It's flat, obviously. And warmer than the advised serving temperature. But on this happy occasion I'm prepared to overlook that.

On a day like this, when the fulgor of the sky steals sighs and Apollo glisters in his chariot, we can certainly overlook that. *Fulgor*. It means dazzling brightness or splendour. Why didn't I? I could have, but it wouldn't have sounded so impressive. As I was, now. Small luxuries must be sacrificed to the gods of the outdoor soiree. Which gods? Soft shadows playing in the undergrowth, a parliament of London plane, the *bon mots* of pleasant company and, of course, that fellow in the leopard skin thong. No. Before Tarzan. Dionysus. His gift, however tepid, must be savoured.

The nose. Bouquet of peaches and wet hay. A ferrous backbone. Tinned peaches, perhaps, left open on a radiator overnight. Late aroma of plastic.

Hampstead is so lovely in the summer. I used to make the pilgrimage up this hill often when Baroness Rothschild threw her parties. Lavish, wild affairs. Yet tasteful. The Baroness had exquisite taste. Drinking a Chateauneuf poured from the bottle is like reading a book without opening the pages, she used to say. Genuine hospitality. Because it should be decanted. To open up the tannin structure. Well that's your opinion, but as a professional I beg to differ.

The palate. More heavy fruit tones. Lurid fructose. Waterbrash. Some white spaces around the edges, chemical, curious. I'm getting sulphur and cat urine. Baize. More American 8-ball blue than billiard green. Thin mouthfeel and the metal still there, poking the tonsils like a fork tine. Tart or corrosive on the finish.

When the Archbishop of Canterbury held a reception for the King of Sweden, His Highness brought a present of traditional

Scandinavian brew that tasted like a trough the village drunk had slept in. So no, it's not the worst I've had. Elizabeth came to that reception with me. She was so nervous in the company of royalty, she spent the entire evening checking her make-up in the back of her dessertspoon and nudging me not to drink so much.

Colour. Under these conditions I'm prepared to overlook this criterion of quality. You can't gauge a person's feelings if they're wearing sunglasses. Criterion. It's a rule, a standard of judgement. Never mind.

Elizabeth was devastated when we broke up. I found her on the porch outside our pied a térre in Portobello, sitting on my Vuitton valise, waiting for me. It was late and I had tasted a great number of wines. Herculean. Andrew, she said, this can't go on. How long must she have waited for me? Her voice was small and tired, like a lost child's. Devastating for her. At least I think she was devastated. She was wearing sunglasses.

Provenance. With this plastic label it's clearly no French domaine. White Ace. Super Strong Cider. Strange. I absolutely did not get apple from that. Wait your turn. I'll pass it in a minute.

I, too, was inconvenienced by our separation, because I did love her. Completely. The little heart wrenching sighs she made when she slept, the symphonies of her own composition she hummed over the washing up, the pout of her lips when I had let her down. It used to make me furious, that pout, but I miss it more than anything now. Funny. I can still see her smile. If you grab at it I will smash you in the face. Inconvenienced because it's hard for archbishops and baronesses to reach you when you don't have a fixed abode or a telephone. Inconvenienced because no one here has heard of a sommelier. They call me "Smelly A" instead, as my name is Andrew and it is phonetically similar. I assume that's why they call me it. It's very witty. Alcoholics are often very witty, though it is not often said.

Final thought. Disappointing aperitif, though not unexpected. In Cretan mythology the Titans mocked Dionysus and gave him a fennel stalk in place of his rightful sceptre. Not unlike me on this bench, White Ace standing in for my Chateauneuf. After the

Titans mocked Dionysus they ate him, so that's what we're up against. Here. Take it. But they didn't eat the heart. Zeus hid it from them and restored Dionysus to life. He was twice born. Twice born. You should be more conservative with your intake, my friend. Don't drink it so quickly. It will lessen your appreciation of the floral notes. It will destroy everything you love. It's a strong point. Super strong. But one that, on this happy occasion, I'm prepared to overlook.

Nonfiction

೮ಶ

I find that by putting things in writing I can understand them and see them a little more objectively... For words are merely tools and if you use the right ones you can actually put even your life in order, if you don't lie to yourself and use the wrong words.

Hunter S. Thompson

A Fish Story

Kurt Caswell

ᛒ

Craig Cass and I were camped at Durbin Lake in Thousand Lakes Wilderness in northern California. It was a moderate 3.5-mile hike in from the Bunchgrass Trailhead under our light packs, packed for a short weekend. We moved easily over the trail through the rolling lava flows, evidence of the recent (about 500 years ago) eruption of Tumble and Hall Buttes.

Some people call him Craig Crass, instead of Cass, but only behind his back because he's this heavy, barrel-chested man, an ex Navy Seal, or so he says "almost" ex Navy Seal, but ex Navy anyway, who went to war in Vietnam, lived at sea with sailors, and did things there he will and will not speak about.

Craig had just told one of his jokes as we sat in the afternoon warmth of the late summer sun facing the lake so we could see it. We were drinking something hot with something hotter poured into it that warmed from the inside out, if you get my meaning. The joke was of the kind that gave Craig his other name, and he liked to tell it about once a month, or whenever out backpacking.

The mechanic says: "You've blown a seal."

The Alaskan says: "No, that's Mayo. I just had a sandwich."

Sitting there at the lake edge in the after-moment of the joke, in the little silence that comes after a joke that asks for another joke or no more jokes at all, Craig heard no more jokes at all and set to reading some fast-paced spy novel with a black cover. Soon he fell into a light sleep, a soft dozing, his head nodding up and back.

The lake was half-full (it had been a long, dry summer), and most of it was a dry ring around the inside of the trees, the bare-boned edge of where the fish might have been. But now, in this kind of heat, in this kind of summer, they were huddled in the center waiting for rain.

Laid back in our camp chairs the way we were, I was staring out at the lake when there, just there, a rounded shape emerged from the woods and leaked out onto the dry shore. A bear. A big black bear. It pressed down into a kind of push-up and drank water from the lake.

"Craig," I said in a whisper, and motioned to the lake with my chin.

"God-damned," he said.

We watched the bear drinking, and we were drinking too, and then Craig said, "Well, if that's not a god-damned bear drinking water from the lake."

We watched, this silence much more pleasing than the silence after the joke, and while we were watching, the bear pressed up into a walking pose, lingered out its nose at us, and then slipped away, dark and silent, into the trees. The ripples from its tongue remained, smoothing out over the water and across the hidden fish.

We looked at each other for a moment, Craig and I, maybe a moment more, and without a word we both rose up and started out to get a look at that bear-place, the place that bear had been, to inspect the tracks so as to be sure. When we arrived there we found it was true what we had seen. The tracks were clear and clean as sky, and shaped to chill the hairs of us: distinctly, yes, they looked almost human. As we left the scene, I turned back and noticed my boot prints, cold and industrial, mingled with bear toes.

But Craig didn't walk back. No. He removed his boots and waded out into the lake where the bear had been, the soft mud-bottom covering his feet, and then as if suddenly air-born where the water went deep, he began to tread across like riding a bicycle, like a bear riding a bicycle across that shallow water-body choked with water plants, as he pressed through them, parting them with his hands, and then he called to me "Aren't you coming in for a swim?" but I was wearing my pants and my boots still and so called back "No," as he worked his way across and came out on the other side covered in green primordial ooze. Noticing this, his creature-hood covered over in green stuff, he waded back in and washed himself off and then tromped a bare-footed path back to his seat. His boots stood empty on the other side.

"Aren't you going to get your boots?" I said.

"Maybe in a bit," he said.

Back now in our comfortable seats, that silence came in again, only this time it was a holy kind of silence and we both hoped the other wouldn't tell a joke to mess it up. And neither of us did. And to consecrate it, we let that moment stand for a long time, a real long time in silence, long enough to feel a little hungry for supper. Craig, he's older than me, at least twenty years better than me, old enough to be my father. But it wasn't like that at all; I've seen a bear with my father and that is a different story. This story is about two friends sharing a bear. And sitting up in the mountains in a basin of lakes after seeing a bear, you feel something in the wind that tells you that everything is going to be all right, that night will fall, and in the morning the sun will be born again, and the rains will return one day to fill the lake and spread the fish out into the trees, out into the place of our tracks and the tracks of bear, and the world will continue on like it always has for near forever. You feel all of this between you, between you and whoever you're with, and you feel it without saying anything at all. Well, that can make a day happy.

An Audacious Eulogy

Wanda Ernstberger

❧

Some stories should never be told. At least they shouldn't be told until no one can exact revenge on the teller. Grandpa passed away over five years ago, and Grandma died last month, so this is my eulogy; only instead of expounding on the good qualities of generations past, in keeping with the Scriptures, I will only present the truth – Grandma was no poet. Yes, she loved Grandpa, almost as much as she loved the church, almost as much as she loved God, almost as much as she loved Jesus, almost as much as she loved people knowing she loved Jesus, but she was no poet.

We discovered that on a Sunday afternoon. At seventeen, I would have rather spent the day perusing the latest issue of *Star Wars* or *Silver Surfer*, but we had to answer the summons to Grandma's – there was no choice. And at Grandma's there was nothing to do but listen to the adults talking, advancing through a field of topics, trying not to step on a landmine. Luckily, we children were usually under the radar, but to avoid detection, I couldn't smuggle a comic book into Grandma's. When Mom was young, the list of contraband material included *The Adventures of Huckleberry Finn* and *Little Women*. The church taught that reading fiction would pervert the imagination, making people believe in fantasy instead of the realities found in the Good Book such as talking bushes, walking on water and rising from the dead. So, if Grandma caught me with a *comic book* – bang! She would explode with holy fervor, demanding that I join the church to savor the fruits of heavenly salvation instead of languishing in my half-heathen status. According to Grandma, Mom was already lost for leaving the church and marrying Dad, but my sister and I were still considered salvageable (Grandma never knew we read *Heavy Metal*).

Grandma's marriage to Grandpa, however, guaranteed her entry to Heaven. When Mom was thirteen, Grandma married Grandpa, a part-time minister, and moved from Boston to Canada. And that day, that fateful day, the family was summoned to Grandma and Grandpa's to celebrate their twenty-fifth wedding anniversary.

Mom's stomach churned for twenty-five days before, hoping she had the appropriate gift, the appropriate dress, the appropriate casserole, and most of all, she prayed her children would have the appropriate behavior.

But, how was she to know? Temptation lurked within the holiest of places.

My grandparents' apartment shone like a pew and smelled like lemon pine tree. In the far corner stood an organ where Grandma played for Jesus seven days a week. As a teenager, Mom was banned from listening to songs like *I Want to Hold Your Hand*, and *I Can't Help Falling in Love With You*. The church taught that the Devil's music would tempt youth to experience the root of original sin – dancing. Dancing ignited the lust lurking in every breast. Grandma and Grandpa didn't even dance at their wedding. It was rumored that Uncle John, their only son together, was a second immaculate conception.

He was there that day, along with fifteen others, including me, my sister and four cousins. At seventeen, Cousin Ray was the oldest, and at thirteen, my sister Bonnie was the youngest; teenagers and adolescents, blood and hormones, water and nitroglycerin, what could my mother do, what could any adult do to head off the oncoming explosion?

We gathered to say grace over salads, chick-pea casseroles and gluten burgers; the church expounded the merits of vegetarianism; control of the body led to control of the mind and purification of the spirit. Ten years before, Grandma and the minister's wife made a pact to go on a vegan diet – no meat, no dairy – to make their bodies as healthy and pure as possible. The diet ended, and so did Grandma's ability to digest lactose. Thus, Grandma developed a pure mind, pure body and a pure case of osteoporosis.

After dinner, everyone was herded into the living room, adults gathering around Grandma and Grandpa, teenagers shepherded to the side. We whispered to each other, what now? The food was gone and the presents were opened. What else was left?

The cake. Yes, we had to stay for the cake.

But, what should we do until then? Grandma and Grandpa never showed movies or played music, unless it was on the organ. With an inward groan, we prepared for a lengthy adult conversation.

But, we were wrong.

Grandma announced that she had a special gift for Grandpa, a gift she wanted to share with the family. She brought out a handmade scroll and unfurled it.

We watched and waited, curious, thankful it wasn't a boring adult conversation.

Oh, but it was more, so much more.

Grandma read the work that commemorated her twenty-fifth anniversary, a poem.

When you took my hand,
my heart had wings.

The universe began with a bang. Life crawled out of the ocean. Grandpa touched Grandma.

Cousin Jeff squirmed. Aunt Cathy glared at him, threatening to burn him to ashes if he made a sound.

Grandma unfurled the scroll and read the next stanza,

When I first saw you,
I heard church bells.

Bonnie let out a little squeak, like a Rhesus monkey. I squeezed my mouth shut, forcing the bubble of laughter down my throat, down my chest, down my stomach, making my gut tickle-burn. We couldn't laugh. God help us if we laughed! Laughing would be tantamount to drawing a Hitler mustache on the Virgin Mary.

The poem continued, each image, each cliché threatening to set us off like Russian Roulette, click-click-click. I didn't look at Cousin Leanne. I didn't look at Cousin Melanie. I really didn't look at Cousin Ray. If our eyes met, like fire to gunpowder, we'd ignite, our laughter exploding through the living room, our parents the first casualties.

Grandma placed the poem on her lap and wiped her eyes.

The parents breathed a collective sigh.

Grandma lifted the scroll, unfurled it and continued to read. The poem went on, stanza after stanza, line after line, repeating over and over,

I heard church bells.

Cousin Leanne stared at the wall, unmoving.

Cousin Ray's breath came in short, hot spurts.

Bonnie crawled under the table, her fortress.

I heard church bells.

The bubble rose up my stomach to the back of my throat, pressing against my clenched teeth.

Then, I witnessed the subject of Grandma's tribute. Grandpa sat silent, hands squeezed between his knees, face glowing crimson. His eyes met mine with a silent plea.

I forced the bubble down, holding my breath until tears streamed down my face.

The poem ended. The children didn't make a sound, survival of the fittest.

Grandma wiped her eyes, touched that her homage moved some of us to tears.

Some stories should never be told. Some poems should never be read. So now I've revealed the family secret: Grandma loved Grandpa, almost as much as she loved the church, almost as much as she loved Jesus, almost as much as she loved people knowing she loved Jesus, but Grandma was no poet. And now that I've relayed the tale, one day Cosmic Justice will cast me into a sea of fire, where I will spend eternity unfurling an endless scroll, reading verse after verse, stanza after stanza, repeating into infinity: I heard church bells.

The Thrill of the Race

John G Fainella

❧

At eight feet long, the cart looked like a small truck. It had been used to carry bricks short distances and had been replaced by a large, motorized, three-wheeled Apone.

It had sat in the dirt, and been rained on for some time, when Carlogrande inherited it. It was still functional and strong enough to take the weight of many children.

For wheels, the cart used steel roller bearings, obtained at a garage, after truck maintenance. It had a real steering wheel, custom welded at the base. Two, thick, braided cotton straps wound in opposite directions on the centre pivot of the steering column so that the front axle turned when the one strap wound tight, while the other unwound loose. The mechanism worked fine as long as the belts were dry, tight, properly set, and the pivot bolt lubricated. Unknown to Carlogrande, the straps had stretched with the rain, and become loose. The bolt was rusty, and steering at running speed was jerky, and required great effort. Dubbed *Carrozzone* due to its large size, the cart had no brakes.

The first time that Carlogrande's gang took it out; he and the children had decided to push it up the paved road on the highest hill just outside the town. It had required much effort to push its weight all the way up to a sharp switch back, where the paved road provided the steepest descent.

The boys were all racing car enthusiasts, and all had experienced, with sleepy eyes, the long, early morning waits for the "bolides" of the "Mille Miglia" to go through the same road in Antrodoco, in the Apennine Mountains of Italy. They longed for the same thrill as the real drivers. The road had taken the lives of several professional drivers who had crashed to the bottom of the treacherous Velino river gorges.

The dangers of steep, reverse-banked elbow turns were well known, but Carlogrande wisely plotted a straight ride where neither the steering system, nor the skill of the driver would be an issue.

There was a mild turn at the bottom of the descent, just before the brick bridge across the river. They could build up to a good speed, and the retaining walls on both sides would keep them from falling sixty feet into the river, just in case.

The first descent was a meticulously planned affair. The hour scheduled for the downhill run had to be in the afternoon so that the drivers of the traffic of 1950's *giardiniera's*, vans, Fiat500's, Ape's, Vespa's and horse drawn carts, would be having their mid day siesta. By two thirty, the morning traffic would have scattered cow, horse and donkey manure, and the sun would have dried it. Dirty clothes were a small price to pay for the thrill; but not to have to wash off green or brown streaks, or the rich bouquet of splashes from one's face, was a greater motivator for the after siesta ride.

All the children pushed the cart slowly up the hill. Carlogrande steered. Locchilù, at the left-rear, pushed with his arms straight out, in line with his back. Sentilipente pushed beside Carlogrande by leaning on the backrest of the driver's seat, and Giovà leaned on the top of the rear-platform as if doing push-ups. The other two boys, Gancia and Faccie, surrounded the edges. Gancia, the youngest, could hardly fit among them all, so his contribution on the climb was minimal. If someone tired or stopped pushing to change positions, the increased weight would be felt immediately and Carlogrande would reproach:

—Push *regà* ! If you don't push, I won't let you ride down, once we get to the top.

Everybody pushed. No complaints. Riding down was the height of all thrills, and no one wanted to miss it.

After a half-hour, the boys were all puffing hard from the effort of reaching the top. Now the excitement would begin. Mouthy Sentilipente began giving orders:

—Ok *regà* lets go . . .

—Wait! We have to check to see if there are any cars coming. Locchilù take a look up and around the bend of the curve — interrupted Carlogrande.

Locchilù trotted up the road and took an attentive look.

—Nobody's coming! — he yelled back.

—*Forza*! Let's get it ready!

The boys steered the *Carrozzone* to face downhill. They dragged the rear axle to line it up with the front. The steering mechanism gave it the turning radius of a large bus.

Before getting on, Carlogrande cautioned that he alone was going to sit at the driver's seat and everyone else was to find a spot at the back.

—But don't jump on before I say so, otherwise you don't get to ride next time!— he warned.

The boys were all excited now, and they were fighting for good positions from which to jump on the cart at the signal. The best spots were on either side, at about the middle of the vehicle. If they pushed too close to the rear, once at top speed, it would have been impossible to run fast enough to get on. They knew this from hitching rides on the back of diesel transport trucks, as they slowed for the climb and speeded up at the top. An older boy had died when he got on wrong, and finished under the wheels.

Carlogrande gave the signal and the vehicle started edging heavily down the hill:

—*Forza, forza*, faster!

—Push harder— added Sentilipente.

Like hungry puppies surrounding their food bowls, wiggling and jumping in strange directions, the boys started running with the *Carrozzone*. It picked up speed quickly. It sounded like an accelerating locomotive. The steel roller bearings hit the hard, uneven pavement, marred by many cracks, and snapped back whip-like, loud, and metallic noise. The wood amplified the lashes into the deafening roar of a muffler-less motor.

Giovà's legs were barely keeping up. Faccie, the fastest runner, was trotting along like a rabbit, but Locchilù, the slowest, had assumed a squatting, half sitting position, skipping along the side easily, with both arms squarely resting on wood. Round faced Gancia, cheeks as red as radishes, was struggling to keep up at the back. Sentilipente had cheated, and was already sitting down beside Carlogrande.

Giovà didn't have time to protest.

—Get on! — Screamed Carlogrande at the top of his lungs. The din of the wheels and the roar of the wooden frame was so loud that those who did not hear, just copied those who did, and all leapt on the rear planks like ants, locking onto a leaf floating downstream.

Giovà felt his left leg slip on the pavement, but he hung on with both arms, got his right leg on, and pulled himself on sideways. All the boys clung to each other, and to the sides of the platform.

All except Gancia.

He had tried to get on too late, had tripped, and rolled head-over-heels twice. He lay sprawled out on the pavement. Giovà was the only one to have seen him and yelled to the others:

—Gancia fell! Gancia fell off!

As the *Carrozzone* sped on noisily downhill, no one heard him. He saw Gancia in the distance beginning to get up and then to walk with a limp. He was rubbing his eyes, evidently crying.

—What a softy *cacarella*. — Giovà thought with disdain.

With no brakes, it was impossible to stop, except if everyone dragged their feet at once. Not that anyone would try while at almost top speed, half way down the hill, and reaching a group of houses. With the great cacophony of metal resonating on planks and elated screams from the bouncing riders, the vehicle thumped and roared alarmingly, as it approached two toddlers playing by the curb. They sat motionless, wide-eyed and dumbstruck, as an older lady dressed in black, hobbled to fetch them. She gesticulated wildly, yelling threats with clenched fists, and uttering severe imprecations —all inaudible— against the women that could mother such daredevils.

Giovà could feel the wind blowing through his hair and he smelled fear in Locchilù's sweaty neck as they hung on to each other.

This was really fast. Faster than he had gone, ever, even on his bicycle!

The road dipped at one point and everyone went —Wooooo!— as the *Carrozzone* 's bobsledded over the gap, and their platform dropped away, leaving them weightless.

At the bottom of the hill, just before the bridge where the road evened out, an intersection split the road. In the direction hidden from view, sporadic traffic led to Rome. To the right, in their direction of travel, cars headed to Ascoli Piceno, a port on the Adriatic Sea. Up the hill from where they were coming, the road went to L'Aquila, another important centre.

Unseen, a *giardiniera,* an automobile renowned for its frame of wood and metal, was speeding uphill towards the fork on the road. Ugo Bompiani, the driver, was a traveling salesman who dealt in leather and shoe supplies, and furnished all the artisan shoemakers in the area. He was hungry and behind schedule. He had left Rome about two hours earlier and was hoping to end the day early by going to L'Aquila, the shorter, straight uphill drive after the sharp turn at the intersection.

But he was undecided.

He could continue on the flatter road towards the equally distant Amatrice, on the road to the Adriatic. He looked at his fuel indicator: plenty of gas to go either way, but L'Aquila had better restaurants and hotels, a more pleasant choice. Bompiani prepared to make the elbow turn to the right by pulling to the left-side of the road. In race-car style, he was lining up his vehicle for a head on collision with the hidden, speeding *Carrozzone*. He readied to blow the horn as required by law on all blind turns.

Carlogrande was grinning with both excitement, and knowledge of wrongdoing. His teeth rattled behind the smile. Going fast was fun, and driving gave him what he craved: power and control; but he knew it was dangerous. At the turn, he steered to the inside and feathered the centre line. He dreamt of being Stirling Moss, his racing car idol, whom he had seen drive on the wrong side of the road, on this very corner.

Suddenly, Bompiani's car appeared before him.

Time stopped as the two vehicles sped inevitably towards each other. Carlogrande tried to steer away, to the right, but the steering wheel would not budge. He yanked at it with all his strength.

At that very moment, at that split second when a decision can change events and the course of history, Bompiani remembered his promise of a roll of leather to a client in Amatrice. It was a back order risking disdainful cancellation, if not delivered today. He readjusted his hands on the wheel and instead of right; he went left towards the bridge.

Bompiani's last minute correction avoided the head on collision. The boys rode towards the narrow bridge, side by side with the car. Those at the back all started screaming:

—The car! The car! Watch out for the car!

With the corner of his right eye, Bompiani had seen a low, dark shadow and he had reacted quickly, expertly swerving further to the left and slowing down. Perhaps a dog had decided to chase him? He accelerated again. Curious, he glanced back through the rear-view mirror.

The *Carrozzone* had flipped over on its left side, across the road, and all the children were sprawled motionless, meters away, in all directions.

A sudden chill ran through his spine.

—*Porco Dio!*—he belched out in horror as he came to a screeching halt, opened his door, jumped out, and ran back towards the scene — all in one continuous action.

Carlogrande had yanked hard, and over steered. He had managed not to hit the car, but he had driven the *Carrozzone* straight towards the wall and then into a fishtail, sideswiping the bridge's retaining wall. The cart had catapulted back into the street and flipped on its left side, throwing all passengers clear.

Carlogrande was the first to get up, unharmed.

—Did anyone get hurt? — He asked as the others began to move.

Locchilù whined —My arm. I hurt my arm…— he was wincing,

holding back the tears.

—*Per tutti li santi*, what a smash up, what a smash up! —said Sentilipente laughing in excitement and unhurt because of his lucky landing on top of Carlogrande.

Giovà had banged the side of his head. He felt dizzy, and his ears were ringing. He rose slowly and noticed a scrape on the palm of his left hand.

Faccie, as light as a grasshopper, hadn't felt a thing. He had tumbled head first through the air but managed to land on his feet without a scratch. His momentum, however, had carried him clear across the street to the other retaining wall, from where he had ricocheted back to the ground. Seeing Bompiani get out of his car and come towards them, he had yelped out a warning to the others. Strangers were to be feared.

—*Oh, oh!* Let's get out of here, guys, that man is angry. *Ce fa 'n culu . . .*

At the entrance to the bridge, amidst thorny blackberry bushes lay a steep path to the river. Unlike the other boys, and with the disdain and open defiance of a losing soccer coach, Carlogrande hesitated to hide. He changed his mind and started to run, just as the big man caught up to him. Carlogrande stopped to face him.

—*Scellerati ragazzi!*— said Bompiani —I could have killed you all. Don't you know better than to play on the highway? Are you the oldest?

Carlogrande didn't answer.

—What kind of example is that to give to smaller children?

The man's tone was insistent and demanded an answer. Carlogrande shrugged his shoulders but he thought it best to concede some kind of an apology, even if just in his tone. Maybe then, Bompiani would go away.

—But I didn't see you. Nobody got hurt anyway — and he turned to join the others, a safe distance away.

Bompiani was shouting in anger and waving his arms furiously. Then, calming right down and looking transfixed, he opened his hands to the sky, as if expecting the heavens to open, recognize his great tribulation, and grant him two well-deserved stigmata. He then turned very human again and readdressed the boys.

—If I had turned right instead of going across the bridge, you would have all been dead! Do you know that? You would have been on my conscience because of your brainlessness. *Madonna Santa*, what a thought! — he added, horrified by the image of his own conclusion.

Appeased by his outburst, Bompiani shook his head and turned back towards his vehicle, now blocking another car.

One by one, the boys' heads resurfaced from the thorny groves. They could hear Bompiani muttering to the driver, stopped to see what was going on:

—*Disgraziati...* they have no fault of their own. The parents should be blamed for these delinquents...

Bompiani drove off towards Amatrice, and the other car approached the boys. The driver shook his head at the overturned cart and calmly showed a modicum of parental concern before driving off:

—Go home, instead of playing on the street where it's dangerous.

All the boys had re-emerged now, bodies expertly wriggling out from the bushes without even a prickle.

Sentilipente, bold and quick with his words, yelled out his trademark, crowning remark in these situations —*Vaffanculo!*— and added the traditional fist and arm gesture of defiance towards the driver, already some distance away.

Turning to Carlogrande, he then asked —What did he say?

Carlogrande parroted in return —What did he say? What did he say? *Gnente...*

He too then raised his left arm in a fist and his right hand slapped the muscle above his elbow. He then uttered a warning:

—Don't tell anybody about this, especially you Giovà. You'd better not tell your mom.

—Me? Why me? I wouldn't...

—Yes, you would, you always shit your pants about everything. You're such a *cacarella*.

The other children laughed, and repeated:

—*Cacarella, cacarella*, Giovà pooped his pants. Ha ha ha ha!

While Giovà tried to re-establish his reputation with denials and protestations, Carlogrande inspected the damage. It wasn't severe. The steering straps had broken off, but this was easily repaired back in town. With a good push, they set the *Carrozzone* back up on four wheels.

Gancia had finally limped down to join them. Since he was the youngest, all looked at the scrape on his knee and tried to comfort him for missing out on the ride. He said it didn't hurt anymore.

Faccie got on to use his feet on each side of the steering axle. All the others leaned into the easy task of pushing the cart home; except for Gancia, who hopped on the back, gleaming with enjoyment for his consolation ride.

It was a time for triumph. The boys began reliving the experience and mythologizing it. They savoured all that they could remember of the biggest thrill of their lives.

—What a ride! —said one.

—*Però che volata regà!*—agreed another.

—And what a stop!

—Did you see me fly off? —boasted Faccie.

—I can't believe we didn't hit that car! *Orate Fratres. Dominus vobiscum et Deo gratia.*— exclaimed Sentilipente in altar boy Latin.

—When are we going up again, Cricri? asked Gancia who could never say Carlogrande's whole name . . .

As one voice echoed the other, the feat grew larger than life and into a legendary *beau geste*.

Word spread that toddlers had nearly been killed, and no denials could assuage parental concern. The *Carrozzone* was retired, disassembled, and the planks used in a chicken coup.

Ironically, as the cart was being taken off the road, the Mille Miglia dream race was also being lifted off Italian public roads. Sadly, five children near Monza, added to the list of fatalities, were to mark the bitter end of the golden age of motor-car street racing.

On Their Salad Break

David Francis

ɮ

They all have short fine hair, tied back, and drawn faces with cruel or at least cold eyes. One is a blonde. The blonde has on a sleeveless – from which her bra strap intrudes on her slender skim-milky arms – flower-pattern granny dress and white tennis shoes. A silver-banded watch and no rings. Holding her elbows in her lap she leans forward with the slightly sick fey look of her profession.

To her left, by the window, sits the oldest-looking of the trio – the one who goes to pick up the food, which one assumes is salad, or pasta, or pasta salad served in deep white bowls that look like the mortar and pestle of alchemists, and their large white cups have the same effect of keeping their diet arcane and secret to the distanced prying eye. Why she is elected to make the two – or three – trips to the counter is also worth losing sleep over.

There are two kinds of people in the world. There are those who self-consciously enter the restaurant, self-consciously select a seat, self-consciously acquire their food and drink, and then sit staring because this is their social life and they have nowhere else to go. Then there are those who are merely stopping off. Butterfly-like, you follow them with your eye, but since they have happened to wander into the panorama and make the blue sky brighter, to scent the air and quicken your pulse – only passing through – you come back from the bathroom, focus, and realize they are gone. Of the latter category are the ballet girls. Should be – but this time they are staying for a while.

They are smoking. Just one cigarette between rehearsals…. The blonde is very young, of indeterminate age, and very flat-bosomed but when she turns her head her beauty is full-blown, fresh and strange like toadstools sprung up to adult size overnight.

Across, with her bare legs crossed, by the window with its sunshiney view of white-iron patio tables under black umbrellas, relaxes (if you imagine a crane relaxing in a chair) their colleague: a dead ringer for the girl in the lefthand corner of Degas' "The Dance Class." Honey-colored hair, tweezed eyebrows, gaunt jutting face, a Norman complexion. Suddenly she squints her face into a pantomime that is unmistakably that of the typical middle-aged French (or German) ballet teacher. A cartoon more real than a realistic portrait. You would know it anywhere. On the backdrop of the glass, silently carping and imitating, as if behind a glass, her oblong head viciously parrot-like. Like a highly-wound string, the repressed mood pops. With feminine alacrity, they grow animated. The face of the oldest stares on, sullen and dark. But that leaves the blonde, as herbal and fragile as the wildflowers of springtime. With a quick upswing, this maiden (one of the Three Graces, no doubt) shoots the finger; one does a double take, but the finger is a direct unhypocritical cultural icon; you can see the tallest buildings of the downtown skyline, like phantoms, from twenty miles away, and the middle finger is about as far-traveling. Hurriedly she lights another cigarette, imprisoned and reckless like a drinker acquiescing to another flat-tasting drink pressured by a shrewd sober bartender before closing time. Oh, if this silent movie was accompanied by a soundtrack, what a noisy scandal it would cause in the quiet fashionably health-conscious room with its New Age muzak, lethargically-revolving fans, and air-conditioned escape, asylum, denial, defeat.

But what is it? I have always thought of ballet dancers as martyrs. Even as freaks. Their hermetic life, forced on them by the one extant instance of amnestied abuse (because misunderstood, rare, and European) is one of baton thwacks to the calves relieved by no social life to speak of – if one means milkshakes and late nights. Their bodies are their medium. Their feet are not their own. They are undeveloped, unexposed to if not unaware of other walks of life. That would be the kiss of death. They simply don't have the time. Still, they fascinate me.

Everybody has his own beauty. The barmaid who teases, which comes naturally to her but not to me – oh beauty is not always complacent, it arouses me out of my humdrum state, and shakes up the atoms of the night. That sad aging woman who sits crestfallen in the bar section when her friend is in the bathroom – her allure is deep as the quest for the truth. The truth of the depths in which one swims, not the tide out of which one skips. The beauty of the guy who sits silent at the party, the only one who sings to the guitar when it's brought out. The uncool one who has soul. The apropos direct hit of a pop song. The peaceful joy of a lull in the afternoon café. The phone call from a friend whom one had given up on. A few words that convince you that this dream life has been remembered.

They stay on. Acting out the role of victims, they are like any group of co-workers out for a drink, restively gossiping about the others. Continuing until every drop of venom is released from fangs wagging at the dummy air. Preaching to the converted. The Degas girl flirts her wrist Spanish-style. Is she mocking a tic of the old-maid instructor, or a dance step, or is the rippling arabesque a tic of her own? They stay on, sipping from the tall cups, smoking, until of an accord like a Daddy Longlegs they rise and tread past the counter, by the alternative newspaper bin, toward the glare greeting the pushing open of the doors.

See them walking away, probably to a car, because even though the bare warehouse-office building that houses their rehearsal space is on the same boulevard, a short walk of maybe two blocks, the brutal heat wave is still on.

Angles

Alan Gillespie

☙

One hand was spread out in front, fingers splayed on the cloth, index twitching gently. The tapered shaft of the cue slid a rhythm across the soft flesh between my thumb and forefinger. The chalked tip aimed arrow-like for the bottom of the white.

My elbow was a perfect hinge, an oiled pendulum, that delivered a straight stroke. I eased onto the table, feet shoulder-width apart, toes lined up at right angles to the shot. My mouth was bone dry. I kept my head still as a bust and delivered the tip into the ball with a sweet ping, following through a good six inches, the white rolling crisply into the black. There was a dull thud; silence; a collected breath; and then soft rustle as the ball dropped over the lip and into the corner pocket.

"Yass!" I shouted. "Gerrit right fucking up ye!" I flourished the cue above my head and necked my drink – nip and coke. I was nursing a hangover. It was half past ten in the morning and I was up 4-0 in the quarter finals of the National Pool Championships.

This was in the team event, which runs on a three-man, best-of-nine basis. There were another two guys on my team. We each played an individual match against one of the opposition. First to five frames would win a point for the team; two points, would win the tie; so you had to hope at least one of your pals did the business as well.

The other two matches were finished. I'd been playing it tactical, taking my time over shots, stretching the frames out, keeping an eye on the tables either side. It was sitting all square with only my game to go. One of my team-mates had slogged to a 5-3 win, and the other had been royally gubbed, 1-5. He now sat on a stool near the bar, chain smoking, pulling at his hair, cursing his impatience (he could at least have dragged his defeat out a little longer and eased some of the pressure). I heard him shouting rabid encouragement between my shots.

A crowd gathered. The pool hall stank of feet and spilled drinks. The carpets were sticky. The bathrooms were like a war zone. Smoke hung near the ceiling, around the light bulbs, creating a mist that rolled down the walls and clung to clothes and hair. The space was dark, with spotlights picking out the tables and the players and the balls. Nothing else mattered. We shunned daylight. Outside people were going to work and listening to music and reading books, but we'd forgotten that any of that existed.

We were the only team to come down from Scotland to Solihull, packed into cheap rooms at a Holiday Inn, living off kebabs and beer and daily trips to Toby's Carvery for arid roast beef and Yorkshire puddings the size of your head. My opponent in this match was a renowned hotshot who had been playing for the England B team. His eyes were keen and he addressed the table with a grace I could only hope for. All the guys were as bewildered as I was at the scoreline. Four up, one to go, and I was playing a blinder. It was one of those days when everything I hit went in. My positioning was impeccable. My potting was spotless. He couldn't live with my safety play. One mistake, and he knew it, and I'd clean up in one visit or put him in hellish trouble with a snooker.

I put on my best Highland barbarian face and yelled "C'mon Scotland!" and some of the crowd booed and my opponent looked like he was sucking on a sock.

There is certain etiquette in pool. I learned when I was thirteen and playing in the pub during the school holidays while my mum worked behind the bar. For example, you must never stand in the line of your opponent's shot. You don't chalk your cue while he's at the table. You always shake hands after the game and you only play safe if you don't have a pot on and you never, unless you've a death wish, balance your drink on the table. Nothing ruins cloth like a spilled pint.

Then there's other things you can do. Things that are best described as 'gamesmanship'. Simple things, like asking your opponent to re-rack the balls for no good reason. You're well within the rules, but it establishes a niggle. If you win, celebrate loudly and aggressively. Makes them wonder if they're as bothered about it as you are. If your opponent pulls off a fluke by potting a ball off four cushions or something, it's a fine idea to demonstrate your irritation. You're supposed to smile ruefully and shake your head, but that only encourages 'em. Better to throw your cue down with a clank, stamp your feet, roar "Ya jammy basturt!" and spit on the floor. Nothing rattles a player quite like the realisation that their opponent is an unhinged maniac.

So I was 4-0 up and it was the fifth frame and it was the English guy's turn to break. I was standing at the side, smug, sipping a new drink, scraping the filth from beneath my fingernails. Pool tables hold an uncommon amount of muck.

Ours was the only game on and they were fairly crowded in around the table. The English against the *Scotch*, as they delighted in calling us. The banter was friendly enough but I held no doubts they would be fucking thrilled to see me lose it from here.

The English knocked in three balls off the break, put his head down and cleared up. It was a simple enough run, with a kind spread and nothing too close to the cushions, but he took it well considering the pressure. 4-1. I shrugged and racked up for the next. There's nothing you can do when you don't get a shot.

I chalked my cue, smashed them, and the white went in off. Foul. The English knocked in a few balls and then laid me in a half ball snooker. Some of the crowd jeered his defensive approach but I couldn't blame him. I had a look at the angles off the cushions but there was no easy escape so I hitched the butt of my cue up high and took aim at the top of the white, slightly off centre. Swerve shots are damned flash, and they look great if they come off, but it's a tricky skill and you've little control over where the balls'll land. I had a few practice swings at it – the secret is to load up on the chalk and don't hit it too hard – and then stabbed down, leaving a fierce blue skidmark on the cloth. The white shot off to the right, straightened, and then curled back, spinning like a globe. I made contact but knocked my own ball safe and left the white out in the middle of the table. The English potted one, hung another over the bottom left pocket, and won the frame after I went for an unlikely long double. 4-2. He gave me a look that said he'd been playing like a kipper but had found his range. I stared into my drink. My team-mates were silent, sitting nearby, rubbing their chins.

He broke and nothing went down. I knocked in five balls but ran out of position. My own fault, overdoing the sidespin, but I scowled and swore and made out I'd taken a wicked bounce off the cushion. I snookered myself by an inch – as the cue ball was rolling, I heard someone behind me saying stop, stop, urging the Gods to let me have a clear sight of the finish. The support was welcome but came to nothing. I could've maybe taken a two cushion escape and had a half chance of making the pot, but buoyed by my earlier success I went for another swerve.

It might have been my hangover kicking in, it might have been an unfortunate kick, but really it was my nerves besting me. I sclaffed it, fouled, and the English didn't give me another look. He

121

was a clever player, up against it, and desperate not to lose to a fat smug *Scotch* git like me. 4-3. The crowd roared aggressively. "C'mon England!" shouted someone. I went to the toilets. Every bowl was blocked up with wet, shitty paper. At the sink I splashed my face.

Rack. Chalk. Smash. Click. Click. Click.

4-4.

When the deciding frame got started, everyone in the hall stood round our table, peering over one another's shoulders. I seemed to drift out of my head and hover up above the lightshades. The table looked tiny. The English was racking the balls. His hands were steady as he squeezed the pack together, his eyes dark, his jaw set. Across the table, picking at his cuticles and rolling the last ice cube around his mouth, the *Scotch* tried in vain to look relaxed. His foot thumped on the floor. His red face was hot to the touch.

They shook hands before the break. All the best, said the English. Aye, said the *Scotch*. I plummeted back into my body. Everyone was watching with sweaty faces and it was 4-4 and I needed another drink and I had been four fucking frames up and it was the English to break off.

I can't remember how we got there but it came down to the last ball. I'd managed to knock in a few easy pots but whenever there was a tough one I'd play safe. My eye was completely gone. The English wasn't much better, he was missing shots, but at least he was taking them on.

He made a mistake, as I knew he would, and left a half chance. Not much more than that. A full length pot on the black with the cue ball about half an inch from the cushion. I bridged on the side of the table with my wobbling fingertips. I prefer to get my full hand on the cloth but sometimes you just need to take your chance when it comes.

He'd turned away. Couldn't look. Was just waiting to hear the click and the drop and the cheering. I slid the cue across my fingers, seeing how it was shaking in my hands. I kept my head dead still. Stopped breathing. Pushed the tip through. Thwonk. I knew I'd missed it as soon as I hit it.

They groaned and I swore loudly at my shoes but didn't have the energy to throw a proper tantrum, which is what I should've done to put him off. My team-mates – I'd forgotten all about them – were mooching about, not sure if they should be cheering or berating me. The English had a shot. Not the hardest. But I'd seen them missed before. Not that I could bear to watch.

I looked out the window. It was a grey day. Wet. Slick, black roads outside with cars trundling past. A housing scheme across the street. A man walking a dog.

They groaned. He'd fluffed it. I didn't look at the table until the balls stopped rolling. I didn't want to see anything but the angles he'd left.

It wasn't easy. The balls were so close they were almost touching, but I had a chance on, up to the top right corner, even if it was a blind pot, and I couldn't be sure where the white would end up, but no matter. I'd had enough of the drama. I chalked, lined it up quickly, got down, steadied myself, and hit it. I recoiled. A push shot. It was a foul. A fucking foul.

The white slid off to the left. The black trundled, slow, wiped its feet on both sides of the pocket, and dropped in.

They cheered. 5-4. Or was it? Some gave me pantomime boos. I looked up at the English. Had he seen it? Had he seen the foul? A push shot is when the tip of the cue touches the white ball twice in the one stroke. It can happen when the object ball is close. But they're hard to spot. I'd felt it, no doubt, in the split second that the white skewered off on a different trajectory.

The English walked over, shook my hand without looking, and unscrewed his cue. I waited for someone to cry foul. A hot hand gripped my shoulder and spun me round.

"Want a fucking drink then?"

Black Fish

Gill Hoffs

CX

"The water which supports a boat can also sink it."
Chinese proverb.

Whether you've found a body or not, when you grow up in a
fishing village you soon associate its blue-grey neighbour with
death and disappointment. Even the happiest of memories have
salt water as a backdrop; in the sad ones, you tear up in sympathy.

The Kennedy Park, flatly green above the Firth of Clyde, lures
tourists of all ages with its stubborn grey castle, toilets and views.
Family fun days had wobbly stalls, an unspoken etiquette, and
village games when I was young there. Football. Rounders. Tug of
war with shopkeepers and fishermen, sunburn, smiles and banter.
Mr Edgar's orange hair glossy as he hauled the white rag over the
line on the grass, ruddy forearms used to winching silver harvests
on board the *Copia* whatever the weather. People fell laughing on
the lumpy football pitch by the stonecast toilet block. His son
stood by with his friends, the teenagers apart from the rest of us,
enjoying in parallel as near-adults do.

Then, ten days before Christmas, there was a problem on
board the fishing boat. Mr Edgar and his partner made for port. A
storm blew up, the boat went down, and two children were left
without a father in Dunure. Lost at sea. Never coming home.

I would see orange hair bobbing along the shingled shore,
heading north past Fisherton, the next hamlet along. Lost buoys
and wreaths of seaweed and sky-blue rope lay tangled on the
beach, with eyes of pink ringed agate nestled beneath.

Dunure is renowned for its Saturn ringed stones and geodes
with tiny crystal caves hidden within. I had field trips from school
there, lots of discussion on the rocks poured from the long dead
volcano across the water, the twinkling quartz crystals, the sand,
shells and stones. Ailsa Craig was all that remained of it, a
volcanic plug covered in birds far out to sea, like the cork left
when a wine bottle shatters, or the burnt-on crust of a pie amongst
the washing up. That half orphaned boy seemed oblivious to the
beauty. Whether sunny or snow, there was always shadow on his

face. Sometimes his friends helped in the search, clusters of them disturbing the oystercatchers with their mourning feathers and peep-peep-peep.

A loner, I walked the walk too, paperbacks in my pockets, a drink in my hand. Who lost this rope? Or this shoe, or this boot? Did he drink from this shard of mug, or crumple this empty crisp packet? The birds would skitter beside me, while the sheep cropped grass above. I avoided the others, and the only mammal's body I found was a cow.

I had walked quite far, past the holiday camp of Butlin's, to the surge of land jutting high above the sea, seeming paused before an inevitable *crash*. Grey pebbles scrunched and slipped below my trainers. I paused to draw a mermaid using a stick in a golden patch of sand. Moved toward the bigger rocks, hoping for rock pools. Amongst some grey boulders draped with dry seaweed flung there in a long calmed storm were the back legs of a cow. They seemed slender and dainty in death, hooves poking up at the enormous sky, dwarved by the height of the craggy Heads of Ayr.

Big black crows hopped about. Most of its carcass lay obscured. I smelled salt air and drying seaweed. Heard the ssshhh of the gentle sea, the popping of gorse seeds, and the activity of the crows. I focussed on the splashes of lichen on the rocks nearby, yellow and orange and greeny-white. Signs of good, clean air this cow would no longer breathe. Leaving the crows to their feast, I watched the tide turn, saw it change its mind and edge closer to the beast. It seemed longer, going home.

Fishing, though nothing like it used to be, is still a major industry here, the salt blood in Scotland's veins. Less than 8.6% of the UK's population lives here yet nearly two thirds of British fish are landed at its ports. It takes its toll, and not just on the fish. Yet it continues, lucky fathers passing their knowledge and gear on to their sons, and the idea of being grounded on land for good strikes terror in many a man's heart. The coast has its own culture, its own traditions and beliefs. Women are seen as unlucky. So are swans, some boats won't even have the matches on board – though usually had a pair in the harbour at Dunure, for tourists to feed and sailors to tut over.

And I remember a summer, after the *Copia*, with pink skies and short nights, and jellyfish stinking on the shore. Mooching round the harbour, watching the boils of anemones in the rockpools by the lighthouse flowering then feasting. Envying the pleasure boats throttling out; escaping. A few handsome young men having a drink in the sun, gathered outside the pub that awaited the sailors' safe return. Light glittered off the harbour's water. Where the damply barnacled walls shadowed it, you could see crabs sidling about, empty shells skeleton white, and seaweed furring up the creel lines. Somehow we got chatting; about the sea, the summer, and what you could do around here. Paul, or Wicksey as he was known to many, reminded me of pictures of David Essex I'd seen in my mum's old annuals. Curly brown hair past a silver-hooped ear, eyes that made you go 'oh!' – if you were a crush prone teenager. Always a smile.

He shocked me. Told me lots of sailors don't bother learning to swim. If it's their time, why prolong it? Fishing is a cold, sometimes solitary pursuit round here. If your boat goes down, well, where are you going to go? If you fall in, either you're lucky and a crewmate fishes you out, or you're not.

Apart from the safety stuff, my jaw dropped at the thought of living on this beautiful coast, with summer warmed water and plenty of rocks to swim to and explore, walking to the edge, and saying 'no'. True, there was a sewage pipe that meant you had to choose your tides wisely, but it just seemed like such a waste. Later, I married a man with summer sea eyes, and heard similar stories from his uncle, non-swimmer and lucky survivor of the sunken *Empire Spruce*. We moved away to a land-locked town in England, and walk the shores with each return, our little boy in tow.

But between that, between the leaving and the marrying, Paul became a hero.

The fish are in trouble: too many are taken, too many are lost. It feels like for every link in the silver meshed dredge there's a rule with numbers, brackets and dots to tell you who and how and when and where, until your bank gets cross and the sea beckons escape.

Shaun Ritchie, 27, was married with two sons, a fisherman with family responsibilities and costly ambition. He bought a boat, the *Equinox*, and sent her for refitting as a clam dredger. After, the welder who'd done the work with him said he wasn't an expert on boats, but thought the equipment looked "very heavy for the size of the boat". With her nose trimmed, the vessel was under twelve metres long. That way, she didn't have to meet the full safety regulations. Investigators doubted she'd have passed the 'roll test'.

As a dredger, the *Equinox* needed winching gear for hoisting up the dredge and a heavily reinforced hull for the half-tonne of catch Shaun was hoping for. Usually this gear is fitted at the rear of the boat, the bow being able to balance the weight and pressure well in a small vessel whose size makes her more susceptible to rolling over and capsizing in the waves. But Shaun had the gear moved to allow the catch to be winched over the side of the boat instead. Burdened with the added weight, when she was returned to Ayr harbour she rode very low in its calm water, with just a few inches between its still grey surface and the deck. People commented on this to Shaun, officials and sailors alike, but he reckoned she handled well...

The *Equinox* usually required a crew of two, Shaun and 19 year old Darren White, but when Shaun had little luck with his catches due to ill weather, a plan was formed that saw five aboard the butchered boat.

Paul, 28, was now living with Pamela Crossan, also 28, and her 6 year old, Kayleigh, just along the street from the late Mr Edgar. Kayleigh had gone to Stranraer for a holiday down the coast with her grandparents, so on the night of Saturday 25th May 1996, Paul and Pamela were enjoying a few drinks in a bar by Ayr harbour. His boat, the *Constant Grace*, was tied up there for the weekend as legislation meant the fleet couldn't work the Firth of Clyde from midnight on Friday to midnight on Sunday. A prawn fisherman and doting stepfather, Paul and his beloved Pamela were trying for a baby together.

It was a lovely night, the weather had turned, and Shaun was apparently desperate to recoup the cost of his boat's conversion. Pamela and Paul had never been on the *Equinox* before but joined him and Darren with Derek Bryden, 20, Paul's usual crewmate. Paul's big brother, Bill, a harbour official at Ayr, had no idea he'd gone out. To fish off the books, for 'black fish' as they call it, meant risking a £5,000 fine. But Paul was a lovely guy, who'd do anything for anyone, and happy-go-lucky besides. With Kayleigh taken care of for the night it was a chance to show Pamela the beauty and reality of what he did every day on the *Constant Grace*.

They sailed south at about ten o'clock that night, the Isle of Arran to the right, the Heads of Ayr jutting to their left, the beam dredging clams and their natural predators from the mud at the bottom of the Firth. It's chillier at sea. Paul lent Pamela his leather jacket, and she sheltered in the wheelhouse.

The dredge had trailed behind the *Equinox* like the train of a wedding dress, collecting clams not confetti below their white frothed wake. Unlike a car, the engine of a fishing boat has a whole vocabulary of noises, not just a growl. If a car has the velvety ribbon of purr, the boat has a rosary of small explosions. The smells of fuel and salt sea life were a far remove from the warm bar they'd left not long before. Pamela was insulated from the noise somewhat in the draughty wheel house, Derek by her side, but it still made conversation difficult.

The guys started winching up the heavy metal cables, bringing their catch to the surface, hoping for plenty of clams rather than empty shells and octopus. Metal, rope, and cable turned and strained and struggled, released a shrieking groan. The seabed shelves in that area, and there are plenty of underwater cables, wreckage and junk to snag the beam as it rakes the murk for clams. It's part of the work, like farmers snagging their plough in a root strewn field. When it happens, you fix the fouled line, you jiggle the dredge free, you sort it somehow or lose the catch.

But then the dredge somehow caught and a cable snapped under the pressure. Already unstable, already straining with the winching, the *Equinox* leaned closer to the sea. The water that slopped onto the deck had no escape. The scuppers, those gaps along the side that let splashes reunite with the sea, had been blocked. Hatches were jammed. It all served to weigh the *Equinox* down. The crew had to fight to maintain their balance on the slippery slanting deck. Paul climbed the metal rigging to clear the broken line but his weight shifted the balance further. Derek, watching from the wheelhouse with Pamela, said to her: "I don't like the look of this," and ran out on deck.

As the *Equinox* turned inevitably into the cold black water, the men jumped overboard. Pamela found herself trapped in the wheelhouse. The door jammed. The boat sinking. No way out. Which way was up? Which way to go? Time slowing in the terror, as if stopping to watch the accident in progress.

Somehow she escaped. A passionate swimmer, winning medals for it in her youth, she swam to the surface. When Paul saw her, he shouted: "C'mon Pamela, c'mon babes!"

She couldn't breathe. Sudden immersion in cold water does that to you, it literally takes your breath away. She clung to the sinking vessel. There were no life buoys on board and nothing else for her to hang onto. The old tyres looped to the sides with rope acted as bumpers in port, protected the boat from scrapes and bumps against walls and other vessels: there was no way to get them off in a hurry. Paul shouted: "Get away from the boat!" knowing she would go down with it if she kept clinging on. He held her up, kept saying: "C'mon babes – deep breaths – keep calm. Let's get some of those heavy clothes off you," told her to take off his jacket. It was dragging her down.

The pleasant evening had given way to a cold, clear night. Stars sparkling, sea beautiful but deadly, with a line of orange and white lights bordering the coast on either side, tantalising but reinforcing the reality of their mile and a half separation from dry land.

None of them wore lifejackets; fishermen find them too bulky and expensive, with a tendency to get caught in the gear. On a calm sea, capsize seems impossible. The boat went down too fast for a Mayday call to go out. With it being the weekend, there were no vessels nearby to offer help.

Shaun took charge, said they should stick together, tried to calm the boys, but to no avail. With seventy feet of water below their shivering legs, and the younger lads panicking, Pamela disobeyed the skipper and made the only decision she could. Knowing their last hope was help from the shore, she decided to swim the mile and a half home.

She was panicking too, but just kept thinking: "I can't drown. It was so horrible … I had gone right under with the boat and I *knew* drowning must be the most awful way to die."

Unlike most modes of death, many have died from drowning then been successfully resuscitated. These lucky souls describe a terrible burning sensation, then complete peace. Calm. Then nothing.

It reminds me of descriptions of drinking raw whisky. I hope it was no worse.

Pamela never once looked back. Just started swimming. "I thought the others would follow me, but then I heard singing. It was Paul and Shaun … singing their daft songs … they must have been singing to try and keep the boys' spirits up. It was awful."

With such a way to go through the cold flat surface of the sea, it was as if she was staying still. "At first I seemed to be getting nowhere and I was no closer to the shore."

As hours went by, the sea grew quiet except for her splashing and gasping in the 8C water.

"All I could think was that Paul wasn't going back to sea on Monday. He could just stay at home."

She was terrified, cold, and numb. The closer she got to the lights of the Butlin's camp, the more she called for help. But nobody heard.

Then, just after 1.15am, Alastair Dick was sitting in a caravan with his fiancée and her mum, down for a holiday from Glasgow.

"I heard screams saying 'Help me, help me, *please* help me now!'"

He called security then followed the voice toward the shore, joining three other holiday makers there, who had also heard her plight.

"We couldn't see anything so we shouted to the woman to keep shouting so we could try to find her. We crossed the fence and went onto the beach and saw her in about three feet of water."

Wading out into the cold cold water, they helped Pamela to shore.

"She could not move at all or feel any part of her body. We took our clothes off and wrapped them round her to give her some warmth. Through the chittering we were able to make out that the fishing boat had capsized … four men were missing. I went back into the water to see if I could locate any more, but I couldn't find any."

She had made it. Rushed to the medical centre, then hospital, Pamela was treated for hypothermia, exhaustion, and a chest infection. Doctors there were amazed, calling it: "A triumph, equal to climbing Mount Everest on one leg without oxygen."

She had been in the darkly drowning water for nearly four hours.

The coastguard, lifeboats and police scrambled with others for a search of the area. The boys were found floating near where the boat had gone down. Shaun washed up five weeks later. Paul remains lost to this day. Only Pamela survived.

Bill Blaikie, still on duty at the port, only knew his little brother was lost at sea once Pamela was rescued from the shallows of the cold night shore. It fell to him to make the call that every parent, and sibling, dreads.

So the legislation changed. Pamela is still a heroine. The men are still dead. Paul is still lost, and a hero.

And I go home with my family, walk along the shingle with its smooth blond patches of sand, walk along, and listen.

Batman Girls

Kirsty Logan

☙

1.

Batman is a game where we go into the spare room and lock the door and strip to our knickers. One girl lies on the bed and the other girl balances on the windowsill with a blanket around her shoulders like a cape and whispers *Batman*. Then the windowsill girl jumps onto the bed so that the blanket-cape billows and we both rub our crotches together until we get a feeling that we can't explain – a tingling, a happy pop low in our bellies. I do not know who made up this game. I do not know why it is called Batman. We like the game and we play it a lot.

2.

We play other games, like Schoolteacher and Shopkeeper, but we're just killing time until we can play Batman again. I do know and don't know what we are doing. I have heard some words in the playground but I don't know if those words are right for the Batman game. I wonder what sort of games other people play. There are a lot of locked doors in the world and something must be going on behind them.

3.

One of the Batman Girls has freckles across her nose and gold studs in her earlobes. Her mother makes pottery and they have a kiln in their garden shed. Another Batman Girl lives above a pub and has a pet goat; sometimes we walk the goat in the industrial park but it just chews its rope until we have to go back. Another has only a mum and not a dad, and another has ballet lessons on Saturdays. Only two girls ever play Batman at once. I do not know whether they play it with each other or only with me.

4.

At school I am a brain. When the teacher gives us work to do I race my best friend to see who can finish first. I am better at English but she is better at Art and Maths, and I don't understand how she can be good at both those things as they seem like opposites to me. My best friend is not one of the Batman Girls. She has three older sisters and once she accidentally walked in on the eldest sister in the shower. Her sister had hair down there. We puzzle over this for a long time. One night my best friend sleeps over and I lean over the top bunk so that my hair hangs over my face and my heart throbs in my throat and I tell her about the Batman game. She rolls over and puts the covers over her head until I stop talking.

5.

When I move schools I tell everyone at my old school that I kiss boys at the new school. I tell everyone at the new school that I kissed boys at my old school.

6.

After university I move in with my girlfriend. During a pre-dawn confession I laugh about the Batman game. She is envious: there were no other children on her street, and she had to learn everything from Science class. I wonder whether it's better to learn things from books or to feel them with your own skin. Sometimes I think I skipped a chapter.

7.

One of the Batman Girls adds me as a friend on Facebook. My profile says 'Kirsty Logan is in a relationship with Susie McConnell'. Susie is definitely not a boy's name. I fear that the Batman Girl will think that I was always secretly gay, that I had constructed the game on purpose, that I had tricked her. That the game somehow made me this way. That perhaps she is secretly that way too. I deny her friend request.

The Lure of Gravity

Moy McCrory

CB

When Primo Levi came to Liverpool in the winter of 1971 it was not as the writer and chronicler of the Holocaust for which he is now remembered, but as an industrial chemist buying electrical conductors for his company. They arranged for him to stay in the Adelphi, a grand white facaded building which then had a long way to decline from the high class Regency Hotel it had been into the sort of place promoting a carvery and disco for non residents that it would become by the end of the century, as its inexorable fall picked up speed. In the seventies it was still an institution which struck awe in the city's natives, most of whom never set a foot inside scared of being in the wrong place, marked out by cheap footwear as much as a foreigner would be by language.

Although the Adelphi was not difficult to infiltrate, very few of us had. Slap banged in the city centre like a visitor from space, this hotel had the power of the strange to disconcert. We didn't know of anyone who had stayed there, but we knew instinctively that they must have been what our parents called 'people of quality' with the automatic exclusion of one's self such a phrase conveys. The hotel hired out rooms to societies for which all one had to do was feign an interest in order to be allowed to sit in one of its mirrored salons with duck-egg blue walls and gilt edged mouldings. But to walk up those white marble steps would induce anxiety in us. Such action could only be the result of a dare. At the entrance we would shrink back imagining fierce warnings to keep out. As with most things it was always the tallest who was pushed in first and that night, giggling like conspirators, we emerged from the revolving doors trying not to catch anyone's eye now that the foyer had been breached.

It was that same winter when Levi stayed there that a group of us, still schoolgirls, followed the hand drawn arrows until we found the music room which had been booked for a public talk by the International Labour League. This would rename itself later as The Workers' Revolutionary Party under the national leadership of a man who would be revealed to have made sexual demands of young women at the London headquarters. He said the stress of the

Fourth International and globalised labour caused him to require 'special' release from pressure without the usual social constraints which he, in his singular position, hadn't time for. He told young women they were helping the international workers' movement. How many obliged? Hard to say, but working class girls generally had more common sense nor did they suffer from the guilt which beset those more privileged. This would have saved any of us, that and the fact he resembled Mr Toad.

That night we were the youngest at the meeting, but we would have stood out regardless- there were hardly any women. The ornate room in the Adelphi was filled with men in grey macs who coughed constantly and spat into handkerchiefs. We were pounced on as *new blood* and only managed to leave after promising to attend a further meeting in the important sounding 'Regional Headquarters' which turned out to be a room full of cardboard boxes over a dry cleaner's near the bus terminus. But each of us had done something none of our parents would have dreamed of, not by going to a political meeting, but in a small way each of us had set the chain of events in movement which would take us beyond the imposition of our backgrounds, simply by being the first of our families to have braved the hotel.

Primo Levi would have been unaware about the anxieties the Adelphi caused. Instead it would have offered him a straightforwardly comfortable environment, one which would be familiar in an odd way to the entrance hall at his family's home in the big apartment block on Corso Re Umberto in Turin. That too has its detailed architecture, highly polished marble stairs and spotless landings. Only the three person cast iron lift in the stairwell disrupts this picture, the same lift he used daily from his apartment on the third floor, and down which stairwell in 1987 he was to plummet setting a debate in motion, accident or suicide, which has not to this day been resolved.

On this, his brief visit to Liverpool, one of his biographers records his shocked reaction to the city's bomb sites. Levi must have been puzzled by Liverpool's inability to recover from the visible after effects of war- a war which had transported him to Auschwitz, and whose physical scars he carried both on his ulcerated feet and in the number on his arm, which he would never remove. Levi was surprised that the flattened sites had been left while his beloved Turin, which had suffered devastating air attacks had put itself back together.

In Liverpool he would have seen the gable ends of houses sliced off and abandoned. These were the open spaces which provided raw playgrounds for us to explore and some of us had grown up in streets where wooden struts supported the end houses from collapsing onto the flattened ends of terraces. Interior walls were exposed with old wallpapers and chimney breasts hanging like so many faded photographs of places where people once lived. When evening fell these outlines of rooms became crossed with shadows and the walls rippled with movement as if families were returning to settle on their worn sofas and listen to the news as they must have in those last weeks before the bombs dropped, carving everything into rubble.

Levi always claimed that it was only luck which had let him survive the Nazi death camps and return to a battered Turin, which echoed with the chip of hammers as the city rebuilt itself. He must have wondered why this city waited for such damage to be redeemed. It was as if the peculiar silences which had followed the bombing raids still hung in the air, grown into decades of silence, suspending over the abandoned sites a fear that there might be worse to fall. The city was holding its breath, waiting for the plummet.

Apparently Levi visited the Cavern. This has to be one of the most unlikely events in Twentieth Century history. He couldn't have gone on a Thursday when it was free to members and we queued wearing too much makeup in an attempt to age ourselves to the bogus date of births recorded on our green Cavern Cards. We were in sixth form, *school* with everything that implied, so we invented jobs. It never crossed our minds to say we were students- someone might have asked us what we were *reading*. We knew the phrase through watching University Challenge. But that was a lie too far, so we passed ourselves off as secretaries and shop assistants who had left school at sixteen and been in steady employment ever since. This alone ought to have made us more suspicious. But at least we got in.

I'm relieved to think that Levi, like us, had visited the genuine club where the Beatles with a different line-up had once played. It was despised by city elders who wanted it shut down because it encouraged 'lowlifes'; musicians and their hangers on, those sort of people. It was demolished. In its place Liverpool got a vacant lot for cars to park until developers transformed the area into a 'high class shopping experience' named optimistically 'Cavern Walks' to lure tourists.

135

Maybe Levi just walked along Mathew Street and looked at the front door. It's hard to imagine a middle aged Italian in a suit going on any of the club nights. If he had, we would have been keeping our heads down, terrified of being thrown out. We might have thought he was a plain clothes policeman.

What would he have made of this windowless place? It was always in darkness except for the recess where they sold watered beer and where there was a single strip light to allow staff to count change and where they sold food which was not for the fainthearted. For Levi, English food then must have been penance enough, but a Cavern burger and frozen chips would have been a serious shock.

Whoever was responsible for his visit should have taken him to Lewises the city's big department store, where on the fifth floor they ran three eating establishments of variable quality. Of these the poshest by far was the Red Rose Room with its white linen table cloths. There was a self service cafeteria, a place locked in the 1950's on account of its wall tiles which had been designed for the Festival of Britain and were too expensive to paint over. It was in here that some of us worked on Saturdays dolloping mashed potato and gravy onto plates. In the up-market restaurant they hired university students to wait on tables to fill the place with out of town accents, any of which (as long as they weren't Birmingham or Widnes) were considered preferable.

What would he have made of the Liverpool accent, this man whose English was sound but was an effort for him to speak? Could he understand what people said around him? And would he have understood the English nuances of class, writ large in the city, even as we were defying our backgrounds' limitations, resisting our own mothers' lives with an urgency which was more knee –jerk than political, more dreaming than driven.

It is recorded that he went to Gladstone Dock. To get there he must have walked along the Pier Head with that smell of chips frying and the mad midget with the oversized head who used to run after strangers in his cripple boot, swinging from side to side shouting obscenities.

If they had any sense they should have recommended he visit the Philharmonic Pub on the opposite corner to the concert hall of the same name. Here a plaque commemorates those members of its orchestra who went down with the Titanic which had docked briefly in Liverpool before sailing to Southampton. In the pub he would have found an environment ornate and stylish and aged.

This would strike a similar note to the décor of Café Platti where as a schoolboy Primo used to stop on his way home, drawn by the array of sweets and biscuits displayed in the shop area. Of course in the seventies the Philharmonic Pub was always busy and impossible to get a seat in the smaller side rooms. Levi might have found its famous interior a sad second to the discomfort of being unable to sit or the struggle to get served at the thronging bar.

Near Hope Street, where he must have walked because he saw the cathedral and noted the homeless people sleeping rough on the steps, did he know the Art College was located, the same one John Lennon attended? And where Arthur Dooley, the sculptor, came to talk and told students that they would get a better training working in foundries with 'real people'. This caused one of the girls, who had by then become an art student, to ask which foundry she would be able to apply for work in, and whose question went unanswered as if she had never spoken. And education was seen by some as part of the class war, in which the young were not merely educated but brainwashed. Better to work in a foundry-whoops, well Missus, *you* could always marry a foundry worker.

Ideas were dangerous. Our mothers agreed. What's all this study for? You'll have to wear glasses and what man will want you then? And if they did, then you were a whore. There was a gender imbalance then in the ageing population of single women whose men folk had failed to return from the war. Yet even those women lost their jobs when such men as did, came home. It's hard to imagine the quiet desperation of single women then, the tranquillised state of mothers, and the anger of their daughters. All beneath the surface of a city, on the night Levi checked into the Adelphi and we braved its marble steps.

Levi, always a gentleman, picked up the pen which had rolled from the girl's bag. Heavily accented he asked if this was hers and light glinted off his reading glasses which were so clean they looked as if they could be empty frames if not for the reflections. He pushed these up on his head out of the way as he glanced up at her. And the girl took her pen back, the same navy blue fountain pen she would write her exams with and thanked this strangely smart and foreign man, then joined her friends, unaware as Liverpool of who he was or that she had encountered her first writer. And if anyone had asked him he would not have said he was a writer. If anyone had asked him he would have said he was a chemist.

"You see that old feller," she told her mates. "He's got a tattoo. You wouldn't think he'd been a sailor, to look at him."

In the Café Platti today the ceremony of the waiters is matched by the slowness of the day. In summer Turin goes onto half time, waiting for a return of cooler days. On this August day forty years after that evening in Liverpool, Levi's city feels like a tired host who is too polite to ask its visitors to go home, but carries on without much effort.

Central Turin is designed with arcades so it is possible to walk through the city without getting wet or scorched but out towards Corso Re Umberto the roads widen and the buildings rise, dark and silent on the shadow side.

The building where Levi lived most of his life still has the family name on the door plate, but his first name has been removed. Downstairs incongruously is a tanning parlour: Tropicana. The man from here wears a white beautician's jacket and trousers, and white plastic flip flops which click on the marble floor at the bottom of the stairwell. He is an unearthly orange colour, a strange guardian of this site, no-one gets past him. Appointments only.

The architecture is solid, the heavy doors and marble steps recall the grandeur of the Adelphi, and like a hotel it keeps its secrets with dignity and discretion. The heavy black lift, whose open work shaft runs up through the building is a monument to cast-iron work. Levi wrote about metals, about their properties, especially those of iron and lead, heavy, industrial, no nonsense substances. He wrote that lead was the metal for death, because 'its weight is a desire to fall, and to fall,' he said 'is a property of corpses.'

It's odd the silence at the stairwell. You can stand there, but the tanning man is sick of strangers and he watches everyone warily. Even if he only protects his business interests he will not let this stairwell be turned into a shrine. And he knew the moment he saw me that I did not want to make an appointment, but he had let main door buzz open and now I stood there. Because I am pale, he suggested light bronze no 1 for fifteen minutes but we both knew that wasn't why I was here. As a foreigner I could only explain in a language he didn't speak. He waited as I crossed to the lift shaft to leave something on the floor there. Sure, he knows who Primo Levi is! One of his books is on the school curriculum, all Italian schoolchildren know. But enough is enough.

I gestured apology to him and walked back out into the sunlight.

I imagined him being relieved that at least I didn't carry flowers. I'll bet he can spot a bunch at ten paces from the other side of the street. As soon as he sees the cellophane wrapping glinting on the pavement outside he must scoop them up and they go straight into the waste. Even if he's not superstitious, most people draw the line at using flowers intended for the dead.

Behind the finality of those closed doors I imagine him, his knees creaking as he reaches down to the floor. When he looks up again too quickly he gets a rush to his head and for a moment the stairwell above him seems to move and he reaches out to steady himself on the lift's iron gate. Why come all that way, from wherever she did, just to leave an old fountain pen?

The tanning man will have cleared it away by now. Dots swim in front of my eyes as I look up to the delicate patterns on the highest levels of the building, out of sight, intended for birds, a reward for defying gravity's pull, the weight of lead, to which we all eventually succumb.

From Russia With…

Julia O'Byrne

CZ

Everyone around me on the Air France flight from Paris to
Moscow drank a small bottle of wine with their meal. Under most
circumstances, I would have been one of them. But I was nervous
about landing all alone in a place where I didn't speak the
language or read the alphabet, and even though a little wine
wouldn't make a difference, in fact, it would have probably helped
settle my nerves, I held back. It turns out getting through customs
and immigration was the easy part. Before I left I was dreading the
awkwardness of the initial encounter with Peter (would we hug?
have anything to say? still be attracted to each other?) but felt sure
that once it was over, everything would be fine. It turns out those
initial moments were the best interaction we had the entire trip.
We hugged, and smiled, and for a second everything seemed like it
would be great. But then we left the arrivals lounge and while
headed for the train that would take us into Moscow, Peter
explained he was sick with a cold and that instead of going out
exploring that day, he'd prefer if we went straight to his apartment.
After I'd bought my ticket to Moscow two months before, I'd
imagined our first night over and over. We'd walk around Red
Square first, then go have a long, leisurely dinner somewhere, then
head back to his place in twilight. It was late June and the sun
didn't set until after 10 pm, its glow lingering a long time later
still. Disappointment settled over me, but I smiled weakly and told
him that was fine.

I'd long been fascinated with Soviet and Cold War history and
wanted to visit Moscow, this mysterious city that ruled over a
country that spanned continents. Growing up in a world where the
United States has been the world's undisputed sole super power, I
longed to see the country which had been the last to challenge that
position. What had the Soviet Union been like? How did it start
out as a place with a noble cause but then descend into a stark,
controlling society with no tolerance for dissent or difference?
Going to Russia seemed like the closest I would ever get to finding
out. It also helped that Peter was there – both because it gave me a
place to stay, and a chance to see if the romance we had started 20

months earlier still had life. I'd last seen Peter in Washington, DC where I was doing an internship. I'd only met him once before, when we'd gotten drunk together with some mutual friends at a Christmas party in Berkeley, at the end of the semester he graduated. We'd stayed in touch and when he told me he was thinking of taking a trip to DC, I told him he should come. He spent two nights and one day with me, before driving off into his future, which included moving to Moscow. And now here I was, I'd caught up with his future, but was unsure if I liked what I saw.

After we dropped my bag at Peter's apartment, we walked around the park down his street. Our conversation, which had come so easily in DC, now stuttered then stopped, like a toy car running out of batteries. We then went to the grocery store, something I always like doing in new places. It was my job to get soap, and liking options, I found him in front of the yogurt and held up raspberry flavoured in one hand, cucumber in the other and said cheerfully "which one?" Peter replied, not even disguising his irritation, "can't you just get plain?" My cheeks on fire, I found a plain soap and silently dropped it in the cart. Back at his apartment, he ordered pizza (so much for trying Russian food) which arrived 45 minutes later, cold and bland. We ate in front of the TV, set to a channel showing *Mr. and Mrs. Smith*. The dubbing was off by a few seconds and if I listened hard enough I could catch the original English voices before the Russian overpowered them. During the next four days of my interactions with Peter I kept doing the same thing – straining to get at the undercurrent, the real meaning of what he was telling me, before his words took over.

After the movie ended, Peter yawned loudly, apologized half-heartedly for being a bad host, and told me that he had to go to bed. It was 9 pm, and only 7 in Paris, where I'd come from. I took refuge in the kitchen, reading for a while. Then I sat on the windowsill staring out at the slowly darkening sky. Exactly a week before, on the Summer Solstice, I'd been in Place St Georges in Paris with my friend Cassie, full of hope and telling her how much I couldn't wait for Moscow. That night was now a mirage, I'd blinked and it'd disappeared. Who was this person I had come to visit? It was clear I didn't know him. From the kitchen window, I could see one of the Seven Sisters – the seven skyscrapers built in the Stalinist style located all over Moscow – and I watched it for a long time, its lights blurring through my tears.

The next morning (and then the morning after that) Peter felt too sick to go out with me, so armed with two maps – in Russian and in English - I set off sightseeing. I got places by counting the number of metro stops between destinations, and trying to compare my two maps. The escalators descending into the fancy cellars of Moscow, with their grand chandeliers and tiled floors, chic salons from which to wait for the metro which bounced – much like riding a horse – over the tracks, were the longest I'd ever seen. Most people didn't walk up or down them, preferring to just stand in place and let themselves be slowly transported. In the mornings when I was going down, I stared across at the opposing escalator carrying people up. The first few times I locked eyes with someone I'd smile, not realizing until the third or fourth person that although they held my eyes until we were out of each other's sight, no one ever smiled back. The first few days were grey and cool, which made everything seem bleaker. I saw the things I was supposed to – the Kremlin, Red Square. But I most enjoyed going to the bottom of one of the Seven Sisters, circling its base, and staring high up to the top; and visiting Patriarch's Ponds (really only one pond). Apart from a few old men sitting on benches, I was the only one there and as I walked around the entire pond – the water grey like the sky, grey like my mood - I sank into the tranquillity and quiet which I hadn't found anywhere else in Moscow.

When I didn't take the metro, I walked, through the crowded, car filled streets. I saw a man standing next to the back of his van, which was open, with little boxes of strawberries laid out in rows. I would have walked right past him but the flash of red caught my eye. The display reminded me of this man in Santiago (where I had spent a semester abroad in college) who always spread his strawberries and raspberries on a pink blanket on the sidewalk outside of the grocery store, trying to entice people to buy from him instead. I bought berries from him several times a week, and though he didn't know my name or where I was from, he knew I loved berries. (Moscow in general reminded me of Santiago. The same expressionless people, the same congested, car clogged dirty streets, the same feeling of not belonging, the same longing to be somewhere else.) In North America, fruit stands are the things of country roads and farmers' markets, the latter being regulated, controlled. I bought two packages of strawberries from the back of the van in Moscow because it reminded me of Santiago, and because I wanted something bright and colourful to liven up the greys and browns of the city that surrounded me. That night back at Peter's apartment, I washed, cut up and then ate the strawberries, wondering if such luxuries ever existed under the Soviets, if sometimes despite the bread lines and the lack of toilet paper, one could somehow obtain fresh strawberries.

Peter's apartment was on the fourteenth (and top) floor of a building without stairs. The elevator was small and claustrophobic and whenever I was in it I crossed my fingers and wished over and over that the doors would open at the right floor. Looking back now, safe with the knowledge that the elevator always behaved properly and I always did get out, I think I should have wished for other, more improbable things, like the elevator transporting me to a different country altogether, the doors opening to a penthouse apartment in Paris, filled with big windows and lots of light, and all my friends holding glasses of champagne, saying when they saw me – 'what took you so long?' Peter had just moved in the afternoon before I arrived, and the apartment smelled like both must and mothballs. It had two layers of front doors. The first was normal, but led you to a small space, barely big enough to fit a body, where you were confronted with the second door, which opened into the apartment. The second door had thick padding, covered over in burgundy coloured leather, which I could only assume had been used for soundproofing. What kind of secrets had been concealed in this apartment? Had the people who lived here believed in the state or worked against it? That their ghosts still exerted power was evident, as Peter and I behaved like spies were everywhere; that even the double doors and the soundproofing couldn't keep them out. We moved around quietly and said little. Any spies would have had little to report other than my crying, long silences, and the low hum of the TV. When I'd come back to his place after a day of sightseeing, I was never sure which felt more oppressive – the city outside or the atmosphere within the apartment, heavy with unsaid words, lost hope and misplaced feelings.

The only things in the kitchen were little teacups left by the previous inhabitants. In the evenings, I'd stand at the sink and wash the teacups over and over, the water swirling and swirling. Every time I thought the cups were finally clean and I turned off the tap, I'd hear Peter and the TV in the next room and I'd put the water back on, and start all over again.

Despite (or perhaps because of) being alone, I was approached by people (usually men) speaking to me in Russian on numerous

143

occasions. I assumed they were asking me questions but I was never sure. They rarely smiled, and usually seemed vaguely annoyed. Peter told me to say, in English, "I don't speak Russian" but I preferred keeping quiet. Speaking a different language would betray my true identity, saying nothing felt safer; it let me blend into the crowd and pretend I just hadn't heard, instead of just not understanding. I felt out of place and alienated in Moscow, but in that respect I wanted to fit in.

By my third night there, things were much the same, if not worse. Peter had built a moat around himself and wasn't letting me across. I was tired of waiting for him to change, and wanted to salvage what was left of my trip. So I told him I would go to St. Petersburg on my own a day early, instead of waiting for him. He came with me to buy the St. Petersburg train ticket, the first time we'd been outside of his apartment together since the first day. He suggested we go early, but then wondered aloud, "but what'll I do between getting the ticket and going to work?" I swallowed my shock and retorted "you could hang out with me." Which is what he did. At a generic café, he ordered coffee and a muffin and I ordered nothing, too nervous to eat when I had so much to get out. I brought up DC and how part of why I had come to Russia was to discover if we had any intensity left. Peter looked at me condescendingly and said "DC was a long time ago." He paused, "And I'm seeing someone now." I wanted to ask him why he hadn't told me sooner, why he'd let me come, or at the very least why he hadn't just been open about everything from the moment I got off the plane. I was sure it could have been a much better trip had he only been honest with me. But I didn't bother. This Moscow Peter seemed meaner than the one I'd known before, and my feelings were already too fragile. Instead, I left the café and began to cry. I wanted to stop, but all I could see and feel was the Peter sized shape in my heart I'd been carrying around since that time in DC, and how this Peter didn't fit it anymore. I went back to Patriarch's Ponds, completely transformed, now that the sun had come out. Groups of Muscovites sat on the green banks of the pond, talking and laughing. I sat there too, feeling I knew the pond better now that I'd seen it in good weather, and bad. That was the problem with Peter, I realized, I'd only known him for a few days in abnormal circumstances, which suddenly didn't seem like enough to base my intense feelings on or plan a trip to Russia for.

I had lots of time to brood on the long train ride to St Petersburg, although I played peek-a-boo with a little girl sitting in front of me – the first Russian to return my smiles. It was nearly midnight and still bright when I got off the train. Though I had called from Moscow to book an extra night and say it was just one person, the people at the hotel asked me three times where my companion was. When they finally understood he wasn't coming, a woman came in to my room and stripped the sheets off his single bed (pressed next to mine to make one). I watched her closely, unsure whether to laugh or cry.

St. Petersburg was everything Moscow wasn't – smiling people, beautiful canals, green parks all over. An old man jogging in a park spoke to me in Russian but seeing I didn't understand, laughed jovially and went on his way, such a different reaction from the ones in Moscow. I didn't take the metro in St. Petersburg, instead walking everywhere: over bridges, along the water, past fountains and statues. I didn't want to go down, either below the city, or into myself, preferring to stay above, basking in the sunshine. I couldn't entirely escape thoughts of Peter, of what a bust this trip had been, of how I had to let go what I had held on to for far too long, but I tried. Finally on my last afternoon I sat in a park with my diary, revealing all the sorry details, sorting out what I could from the mess of emotions and contradictions that filled the week. After a while the sun felt too bright, so I put my diary away and walked on.

I live in Montreal now, and Parc Lafontaine reminds me of Patriarch's Ponds. Whenever I walk by, I begin to dwell on those melancholy days I spent in Moscow, forgetting that I at least had better days in St. Petersburg at the end. I had such high hopes for seeing Peter, for understanding Moscow, and I wonder now how I ever thought either of those things would be possible in a few days.

Valachi Expose'

Bob Tomolillo

ΟΒ

I was eleven years old when the Valachi papers were published in 1963, but I can still remember the impact it had on my father, as he stared at the photos of the indicted wise guys on the front page of the newspaper. An alarming number of the Italians, accused of associating with 'La Cosa Nostra', actually lived on the next street, in an exclusive development where houses had manicured lawns, decorative brick fronts and in ground swimming pools. A low level criminal, Joseph Valachi gave the first public testimony of underworld activities, revealing a widespread criminal enterprise that influenced politicians, controlled labor unions, and performed other illegal activities.

"Isn't that Kathy's father?" my mother inquired, in a hushed tone to my dad, who leaned over the newspaper eating his dinner.

The father, of my sister's best friend, was included in the line-up positioned second from the right. Under the photos of the men were their given names along with all of their known aliases. Some of the nicknames sounded comical and had the effect of dampening the severity of their crimes, but it wasn't until this "expose'", that we were faced with the reality that criminals existed in our midst.

Valachi, publicly revealed secret ceremonies, and the code of silence, that new members of the crime syndicate were sworn to uphold. That there was a criminal network exclusive to Italians gave form to many of the activities that we witnessed on a daily basis, and caused many Italians to distant themselves from what was becoming a blight on the community. For my father, it represented another roadblock to the happiness he worked so hard to achieve.

We were a working class family, twice removed from the mainland, after my grandfather emigrated from Italy in the early 1900s. We lived in an Italian enclave, a few miles outside Boston, in a two family home owned by my grandparents, and then moved north several miles into a new house after the fourth child was born. My early years were spent in the first floor apartment of the two-family home, where I shared the only bedroom with my sister.

The rear yard became my sanctuary; a small patch of land with wild rhubarb, a few tomato plants and an elderberry tree that peppered the grass with ripe berries in early summer. In this quiet refuge, I heard my grandfather and the neighbor speak the language of the old country, as they leaned over the wire fence that divided the lots. Their conversation possessed a calm, sweetness of tone that reflected the deep respect the two men held for each other. The kids were never encouraged to learn the language, because my mother had a plan for all of us; being Italian was secondary to earning a living and raising a family, and a real education required that we speak the language of the land unencumbered.

My mother grew up in a blue collar neighborhood, acquired a basic education, and never lost her passion for learning. She developed an aristocratic manner, after being exposed to the world of books and music by her older brother. During one of our many family excursions in the 62' Plymouth station wagon we drove through a late night winter snow storm. In the distance, the road barely visible, my mother caught sight of an object in the snow. My father stopped the car and crossed over the road to investigate. Lying helplessly was an elderly woman, who had fallen onto the sidewalk. We sat quietly in the dark until my father returned to the car.

"Was she inebriated?" my mother asked, as we resumed our ride.

It was typical of her to use an obscure, well placed word, to shield us from life's hardships. Her response displayed a civility and respect for us that instilled a curiosity for words and the power they affected. We continued our drive into the snowy night, leaving the children to ponder this simple act of compassion.

My father was a man of moderation, a steel worker, and veteran of the 'Great War'. Upon the death of his young mother, he became a 'ward of the State', when his father left the ten children to fend for themselves. The young boy was sent away to live on a farm in Western Massachusetts and remained there until his older brother was able to take him in. My father's main focus was to embrace his loving family, as he sought to rebuild his broken childhood, and erase the memory of his alcoholic father. I would on occasion get a glimpse of his painful past, during one of our 'teaching moments', when after being scolded by my father, he would soften his tone and explain how hard his early life had been. I sat upright, stoically enduring his outburst, until he began to speak about his past. Tears began streaming from my eyes as I became touched by his sadness and the disparity of our lives. In one, defining childhood event, he recounted the rejection he felt when he found himself sitting alone on the trolley, across from his father, who refused to acknowledge him. My dad was a man unable to disclose any weakness, but he held a certain melancholy that made him more human, more loving, and ever thankful for what he had accomplished.

It was comforting to grow up in a neighborhood with people of a common descent. Back then, many Italians were aware of a family member who associated with 'La Cosa Nostra', we just didn't have a name for it, until now. Valachi's expose' had the effect of imposing constraints on Italians who worked hard to insulate themselves from the criminal lifestyle, but ensnared others who became fascinated by the lawless group. In a family of ten brothers and sisters, it wasn't easy to remain a neutral observer, and it was understandable if a member of the family went astray. We reluctantly greeted cousins or uncles known to be affiliated with the mob when we came together at the funeral of a deceased family member, During the funeral of my favorite uncle, who had been a captain in the local police, I met cousin 'Ralphie', who did 'time' in Walpole State penitentiary for his suspected role as 'hit man' for the crew. Ralphie was inconsolable, as he recounted heroic stories about our uncle, a fitting memorial to one who had 'saved his ass' on numerous occasions from going to jail.

As children, we didn't know what to think when Angela's dog dug up a bag of money in the back yard where we played. We chased the dog as it ran in circles, while pieces of the musty bills dropped from its jaw. Looking back, I wondered why my friend's dad, ironically a member of the state police, spent hours on the telephone writing numbers down on scraps of paper. Or, when I traveled across town to visit another schoolmate, and found that the front porch of his home had been transformed into a department store, with boxes of items for sale. There were shoes, sneakers, and racks of men's suits lining the walls of the small apartment all at a reduced cost.

After a winter snowfall, we would walk around the corner to the new development, and earn money shoveling snow out from the long driveways. We became familiar with each of the owners, and noted all too often their sudden disappearance, marked by a caravan of black limousines, waiting along the street, as the young widow, dressed in a stylish black skirt and high heels, walked casually from the home.

Events such as these were commonplace, and may have continued without Valachi's public decree. The contribution that my family made to a moral society was vindication of our connection to the wayward members of our culture. We thrived, and gained our respect through simple virtues. In time, diligent law enforcement curtailed the activities of 'La Costra Nostra', and as a result diminished the bias, that honest, hardworking Italians, bore as a reward for their success.

Collaterals

Mary Wilson

☙

In 1960 South African Police fired on peaceful Black demonstrators, killing 69, many shot in the back.

It was strange to see both parents on the platform to meet us - usually it was Mom only. Veronica, my sister, and I were so excited after the long journey from our convent boarding school that we flung ourselves out of the carriage door into their arms even before the train stopped. Hugs and kisses all round.

Dad was South African Ambassador to Sweden. I was a naïve 14, my sister four years younger.

We followed the porter to where Smitty, in his peaked chauffeur cap and grey jacket with epaulettes, waited by the black Mercedes.

"Smitty! Smitty!," we yelled. He nodded and loaded our cases into the boot. Dad sat in the front, we on either side of Mom in the back.

Veronica bounced about. "It's holidays! And our friends are here!" We were part of a group of lively, spoilt expat brats. She chanted: "No more Latin, no more French/No more sitting on a hard school bench."

We became aware of silence. Dad turned and said: "Something terrible has happened." Smitty's shoulders shot up to his ears.

"Is Grandma dead?" Veronica burst out, tears flowing. "Oh no! She mustn't be dead!" she wailed.

"Sssh, sssh … No, she's fine – we spoke last night. She sends her love."

"Is she sick?" I persisted. Grandma was so special and grown-ups are inclined to lie.

"No, she's OK – I told you so."

Smitty drove through the Stockholm traffic and, after dropping Dad off near his office, stopped at our apartment block that overlooked a quiet little square. He held open the ornate front door. The lights for the lobby and curving stairwell came on and the door closed slowly behind us with a pneumatic hiss. The lift was an old-fashioned, cage type, with two concertina metal gates.

Ours was the only door on the third landing. Two flats had been knocked into one for interleading reception rooms, study, kitchen, and maid's quarters. On the floor above, accessed via internal stairs, were our living quarters which were more homely, especially the sitting room, because Mom insisted on bringing our own well-worn furniture and pictures to every posting for some continuity in our gypsy lives.

The top floors housed the secretive, silent Chinese Embassy.

"We've had an extra, strong lock put in – this is the key. Remember to turn it twice," Mom said.

Inside, the telephone rang, maybe one of our friends. Mom took it. She turned bright red and slammed down the receiver.

"I'm going to lie down for while," she announced.

We ran up to our rooms. Mom always prepared a surprise for our homecoming. Each bedroom was filled with little vases of fresh flowers and 'Welcome Back' cards she had made, some with appliqués or decoupage, others with pressed flowers or her own drawings. And the treat this time was little cakes and biscuits on pretty plates. We took them down to share with Smitty and Helga. He was alone at the kitchen table.

"Where's Helga?"

"She's left. You're getting another maid."

"But I liked Helga," whined Veronica, crying again. (She was very teary at this stage but soon toughened up.)

"Why has she left?"

"Your Mom and her had a row."

"What about?"

"Helga raised her voice to your Mom."

"Why?"

"About what's happened." He paused. "Your Mom said she was a fine one to talk what with the Jews and all."

"What's Jews?" Veronica snivelled.

"Like Jesus," I snapped. "What did Helga say?"

"Jesus was dead but he rose again. On the third day," my sister recited.

"Not this lot, they won't," said Smitty. "Look – just leave it for now. Helga's packed her things and gone."

"Where?"

Smitty shrugged and went back to his newspaper, quickly turning over a page full of photographs. He was the grandson of a

Boer prisoner-of-war on St Helena who had chosen to remain on the island. Smitty still spoke some Afrikaans. He had been at sea until he married a Swedish woman and learnt the language and trained as a Mercedes mechanic, useful skills in his present job.

We went upstairs again to unpack – not very well without Helga's help. I read for a while, then dozed off until I heard Dad come upstairs.

I slid behind the full-length curtains in the corridor.

"…whisky, neat, please. Did anyone phone again?"

"No," she lied,. "No-one. What are you going to do?"

"I can take it if it's not personal. It's my job."

"Vicious devils, aren't they? Devils, bloody evil devils!"

"Some are, and they should know better."

"The editor and that damn politician?"

"Those two especially - they're orchestrating it. They attacked us again today, mentioning me by name."

The telephone rang. Mom listened.

The Lundbergs. Asking whether we would mind not coming to dinner on Saturday. She says that some of the other guests object to our presence."

"Now we'll find out who our real friends are."

"Supper's in the kitchen, I'm afraid. Such a long time since I cooked a full meal."

"Kay, the girls must know nothing about all this. They're too young to face something so dreadful."

"Should we send them back to England? The aunts will have them, I'm sure." These were our great-aunts who took us in during exeats and half-terms. They were sweet and kind but very old. We would rather be here – after all, what had we done wrong?

"It'll all die down soon. They'll find someone else to persecute," Dad said.

We were really looking forward to the tennis season. I was shaping up as quite a good player and I loved the game and worked hard at it. Dad always got tickets for the big matches, with some to spare for his staff.

After supper Dad announced: "Anyone for tennis on Sunday? South Africans are in the men's doubles."

We put up our hands, shouting eagerly, "Yes, yes!"

"Is that wise, Jack?"

"We must show support. Life continues as normal. Nil carborundum illegitimi." I knew what that meant, although my teacher had told me that it was bad Latin.

After supper we sat together reading. Dad kept half an eye on the flickering black and white images on the mute TV, incomprehensible anyway because none of us spoke Swedish.

"I don't want you two to answer the phone," Mom said.

"Why? How are we supposed to contact all our friends?" I asked sulkily.

"You can phone them."

"But they can't phone us?"

"They can, but you can't answer until Dad or I have identified who it is."

"But…"

"That's that! Listen to your mother! No more of this," Dad said. I was shocked, my sister wide-eyed – Dad was seldom sharp with us.

The phone rang right through the night. Our parents looked red-eyed and shaken next morning. When we were alone, I picked up the receiver but it was dead although I tried again several times.

Bored, I went onto the balcony. Today there seemed to be more people in the square than usual.

The next day when the phone rang, Mom answered. "It's Marta." My Spanish friend, back from her convent. We chattered excitedly and she invited me to a party. "Everyone's coming," which sounded good – all my friends.

Every night our sleep was continuously interrupted by the ringing of the phone, followed immediately by a 'ping', meaning Dad had cut off that devil, as we were now all calling them. Mom's explanation was that Dad needed to keep in contact with head office.

Veronica solemnly informed Smitty that Dad was cutting off the devils' heads. He replied that he first hit the devils hard with the car, then ran them over so that they were squashed flat. We shrieked with delight and asked him to do it for us.

"Not if your parents are in the car. It might upset them, so don't tell them." We shook our heads.

Ever more people seemed to be in the square, just milling around.

Mom had forbidden to us to go out alone, not even to play in the square or to the shops in the next block. We soon were bored. We invented 'angels and devils' - 'cops and robbers' with a surreal religious twist. We took turns at being Archangel Michael, armed with a candelabrum as trident or bolt of lightning. His broadsword was a fish slice and his helmet a rose bowl. The rest of his armament also came from silver engraved with the South African crest – a springbok and a lion rampant and, ironically, the motto 'Ex unitate vires'. We hurled milk jug grenades, teapot bombs, and ashtray mortars.

Whoever played the devil got more mundane attire – two red-crayoned paper cups held on with hairclips were his horns and for his tail we plaited red wool leaving a knot and a tassel on the end. The devil came in many guises but without further visual detail, he got kitchen utensils as weapons.

We tore through the formal rooms and constructed barricades out of cushions and any antique furniture light enough to drag around. When the Archangel won, she snipped off a piece of the devil's tail and stood with a foot on his head.

Our parents were too preoccupied to notice. Mom was tense and irritable and snapped at us for nothing at all. Dad returned late via the service lift, looking grim and saying little. We learnt to keep quiet.

Mom issued a new prohibition: we were not to look out of the front windows after five o'clock. To ensure this, she closed all the curtains. It felt like winter again.

However, she couldn't isolate us entirely. We could hear shouting and occasional banging of drums. I peeked out of the curtains and saw the street full of people gesticulating at our building, some carrying placards.

"I think these are the devils." Veronica looked terrified. "Don't worry. You and me and Smitty and Archangel Michael will conquer them," I said.

Eavesdropping again behind the curtains, we heard that someone had tampered with a lift cable at Dad's office and the Fire Brigade had to rescue the terrified passenger. "They made us feel it was our fault," said Dad.

So the devils were there as well.

One night we leapt out of our beds when a succession of explosions went off right outside. "Get down! Get down!" Dad shouted and we cowered into a corner, shielded by Dad's wide arms and strong back. Then loud hisses and sparkling lights penetrated the edges of the curtains and we laughed with relief. The next morning scorch marks were on the façade of the building.

The day of the tennis match, Smitty arrived just after lunch. "Whatever happens, just keep staring straight ahead. Don't look at anyone. Smitty – I'm relying on you to keep a cool head," Dad said.

"Aye, aye, sir!" he said, with a grin and a salute.

As we arrived at the gates, a screaming horde surged forward to surround the car.

"Slow and calm, Smitty," Dad said.

"I'd like run the bastards over," he muttered.

Mom said, "Courage mes braves."

Fists hammered all over the car. The doors and tyres were kicked at hard. Devil faces pressed up against the windows, distorted into grimaces of pure evil. Mom, trembling, held us tight to her. Gobbets of spit ran down the windows like snot. Men jumped on to the boot and bonnet and started kicking. Others jumped up and down on the roof. The noise crushed in on us and the rear window started to splinter.

"Keep your heads up and your eyes on me, nowhere else," Dad said.

"Bloody police are doing nothing – look at them – they're just standing there. Everyone can see there are children in the car." said Smitty.

"Just get us there." said Dad. "The staff's there to meet us."

The car was rocked from side to side. Smitty, elbows locked, knuckles white on the steering wheel, tried to control it. Veronica and I whimpered but with our mouths closed. I was sure we were going to die.

Somehow Smitty got us through to the tennis court entrance. We pushed ourselves out and were rushed to our seats. Dad's staff sat in the surrounding seats. The match started with howls and boos directed at us, punctuated with incomprehensible public announcements. Mike, Dad's deputy, stood directly behind us, despite complaints from other spectators. He was a tall man and he kept his hands deep in the pockets of his long khaki raincoat. He did not watch the match; his eyes roamed around the crowd. (Afterwards we learnt that Mike, a pistol champion, had a gun in each pocket.)

I soon became absorbed even though it turned out to be a scrappy game.

Rain ended play and dampened the murderous enthusiasm of the devils.

"Thank goodness that's over," Mom said.

But it wasn't.

A few days later Dad dropped me at Marta's nearby. I was so looking forward to seeing my friends again. We were not an exclusively expat crowd – there were also some Swedes who spoke either French or English. It was one of these who, after tapas, invited me to dance. I had rather fancied him from afar and I loved dancing.

He came in close. "How many blacks has your father killed?" he asked.

"What?"

He raised his voice above the music. "I said: how many blacks has your father killed?"

Things stopped. I froze. "My father has never hurt anyone in his life!" I shouted.

I stormed off and cried and cried in the guest restroom. When I saw my red, puffy face, I ran home. I ran and ran through the streets, gasping with sobs, my eyes streaming.

As I got into the ancient lift, someone slipped in through the half-open front door. I slammed both gates shut and smashed my fist on the button. A man was running up the stairs. The clanking, clattering lift took forever. The man was now panting and moving more slowly. I scrabbled for the keys and I flung open the gates. I turned the first lock, then the second. The door would not open. I rang and rang but no-one came. I screamed and pounded the door frantically. The man's head appeared coming up the stairs.

The timed landing light went out. I felt around for the switch. The light showed his ugly leering face and his fist held high ready to strike. My sister screamed my name from inside. I slumped back against the door. The man's hand dropped to his waist and he pulled out a pink, rubbery truncheon with a purplish knob at the end. As he reached out to grab me with his other hand, I pulled my knees to my chest and kicked him hard. He shouted as he fell backwards down the stairs.

Above, two Chinese men peered over the banisters.

I turned the keys again and tumbled into the entrance hall. Veronica slammed the door shut and pushed as I locked it.

"Someone followed me in! He came up the stairs and tried to hit me!"

Trembling, we held each other, and agreed not to tell our parents.

Another afternoon Veronica answered the telephone. An angry woman shrieked in Swedish about Sydafrika. My sister flinched, then vomited.

We added another game called 'Gorgons'. This involved holding expressionless faces and stares until one of us gave up, giggling. As a further refinement, one would pretend to torture the other until she cracked.

The state of siege continued. Mom gave us drawing lessons. The new Latvian maid arrived, spoke very little English and cooked strange food we eventually grew to like.

Our relief on returning to the calm and safety of the convent was tinged with guilt and worry at leaving our parents alone to cope. The nuns were their usual serene, kind selves; not so some of the lay teachers.

During a Geography lesson I raised my clever-clogs hand to answer a question and the teacher snapped: "We don't speak to people like you." At the first tennis practice, the coach, my mentor, pointed to me and said: "Not you – you sit on the 'Whites Only' bench until we've finished." I held the Gorgon stare for a long time but she would not meet my eyes. I refused to play again, even though I was among the school's best.

Teachers too can be bullies.

My sister and I clung to each other during the following weeks, shutting out everyone with our blank faces even the concerned nuns could not penetrate. We concentrated on work, taking praise with the same sullenness.

We were experts now, and we had the shield and freedom of indifference.

Soon afterwards Dad, aged 45, suffered a severe stroke that destroyed his career. We became an unhappy, fearful family. We never spoke about Sweden until many years later when I asked Dad what had happened then to cause so much trouble.

"Sharpeville, of course. Didn't you know?"

Prose Poetry

❧

All my life I have lived and behaved very much like the sandpiper - just running down the edges of different countries and continents, 'looking for something'.

Elizabeth Bishop

Leviathan

Ian Crockatt

CЗ

Thon wee mon

with the hair and hymnbook (to Lenins 1,2 and 3), perfecter of the
lyrical snarl, weigher and recorder of Scotland's languages,
inordinate lacerator of the anglophile ear, acerbic, thistle-tough,
dew-tender,

long-married,

whose witty, erudite, passionate verse
burst contemptuously from Scotland's literary hearse -

thon wee mon

would be something awfie to meet down one of literature's rank
and twisted alleys, (or between the Scottish Poetry Library's
Tessa-haunted shelves)

 i' the how-dumb-deid o' the nicht.

Did he not reach back behind the gift of his name and lug the
whole apparatus of a new Scots language out of his throat, turn this
prickly synthesised tongue into a fuse and hold a match to it?
Bzang!

(Yon wee mon

Would have loved that mis-print!)

 Which puts me in mind of a Berserk in a vest at his one love's
wedding crashing through the tables of wines and meats, kilted

guests flung as passive onlookers out of their seats, the groom
pinned with one hand to the wall while the other reaches for hers,
the silk clothing the silk, a wund wi' wurlds tae swing, saying

For Guid's sake, Jean, wauken up! I'm a poet,
you c'ud mak allowances for that!

'course he was fit fer a flytin', thon wee mon,

any time, any place, with a cocktail of ice-cold thought and
overweening words for his weapons and a phalanx of rabble-
rousers for seconds, any dawn, any street.

Lenin? Thon wee mon

adored but never hurt a flea, exceptin' of course the swarms of
beasties and leeches in the schemies and glens draining the last
few pints from the last few working-class Scottish men, from the
corpses of Gaels and Picts.

Adored, but it wasnae the minister who leaned out of his pulpit in
the shivering kirk tae shout *our concern is human wholeness*

or who crooned in a hymn, of Burns,

the world hath need,
and Scotland mair sae, 'o the likes 'o thee!

If the cap fits, wee mon – despite the electrified heather o your
hair –

if the cap fits.

Skinless Night

Dylan Gilbert

ॐ

We're surrounded by darkness and opium is in the air—just breathing it in, the balmy Manhattan night, creates a floating feeling contrary to dizziness. Backs propped against the asphalt slant at the edge of the roof, merging into the vast skyline. 46th Street bustling below, but me and Leila in solitude with the upper city, lit up and dream-like. To our right, the mighty Empire State Building, stoic and proud, lit up in neon blue. Ahead the Chrysler Building, an Art Deco rocket ship, classy and optimistic, a hundred white-light triangles at the top. And a thousand, ten thousand, sky-bound cement structures, surrounding us, dark monuments, each with its own pattern of glowing windows, some so close we can reach out a hand and touch.

We lean against the edge, the slant of an asphalt lip, but no wall. We blend into the buildings, the air, the night. Our backs against the slope, heads leaning back, not caring about the dirty tar, because we are the tar. Whispering in the blackness: black roof, black sky, black night. Only seeing her faint outlines in the darkness, her curves: a slice of cheekbone, a moon of hip, an arc of breast.

Our bodies side by side, heads to the sky, I notice the space between our legs has faded. I feel the warmth of her leg leaning against mine and feel opium again, racing from her thick thigh into my blood stream, and my heart would normally be frenzied with lust now, but the sky is too big and the city too infinite and it makes me serene with something slower and deeper than lust and the heat from her thigh moves into my body and into my arm which on its own volition wraps around her shoulder and pulls her in close and meaningless words trickle out of our mouths, but the words don't matter, only the sweet tones and soft sounds floating into the night.

When I get up, I offer my hand and pull her to her feet and she leans her weight into me as I swat asphalt pebbles off her back and ass. She clutches the side of my hand and leads me down the stairs to her florescent-lit apartment, her coffin-sized room, and her single bed.

I enjoy the waves of her naked body beneath mine and the soft kisses on my neck. But it feels strangely spiritless without the city and the night.

norwich spring

Emilie Vince

 C3

the pinks and whites i bless them; they bless us, strolling hand in
hand between cherry trees with the scent of cream emulsion thick
in the air, and japanned pink. the flower and the leaf, we wander
delicately in a new dawn led by april's yellow hectares, the world
a gorgeous mote floating in my eye's lazy afternoon, opened on
the day before may hangs its linens out for the breeze to rinse blue
and back to white, with the world losing its wits to be drinking up
new greens.

the strip of moon lying across our bed reminds me of snow in the
orchard in may. my thoughts are wafting across the foolscap page
that i'll tear off, biroed and full with deep pressed marks, to place
on the rustling heap beside the bed. i saw a fox cross a strip of
moonlight once, tracing the dark city as it left the cemetery or
returned to the cemetery, knowing its own roads on which it
travelled. this sure-footed moon lights up the tangle of telephone
wires outside the window, and makes silhouettes out of rooflines
and chimney pots, negatives of the city communicating themselves
to my mind's eye. i should be sleeping wrapped in quilts, but for
the moon's skyhooks urging this city up, away from late
afternoon's curls and the early evening's cool, the turn of blue-
silver dark nudging our hands to each other's mouths, to each
other's sleeping cheeks and eyelids, surprising us into one graceful
leaping self.

you partner my darkness. you take the pull of me and lift it, and i
lie awake writing beside your calmed, hollowed and mountained
form. the moon snatched me awake, stole away the covers from
my mind, and reached its fingers into our bed. with audacity it has
marched me through orchards, lawns, frothy springtime, the fox
slipping through unmanned streets. with simplicity it removed the
props. now i lie unadorned in my bed, giving up my secrets to the
old-fashioned page. i give, caused by the moon to spill; by the
moon and you, sleeping placeholder, holding my mind's eye and
blinking it open. from the depths of dreams you cajole my
moonwoken mind. you catch and note the swing, the lilt, the years

spent cataloguing labyrinths and depths. you catch my spill, and i
hold out these pages to you.

An Invoked Diligence

Desmond Kon Zhicheng-Mingdé

❧

All worthwhile sympathies ruled out, the dakinis are lagging in their step. "Don't mind their petty worked-up fears," the First Dakini says, always discreet, discerning and fully at ease with a public diplomacy. "Look at these ragged claws in the brick," the First Dakini raises the kiln to eye level, "never enough good faith, never enough mindfulness around these parts anymore." Give Mount Olivet a cenobitic reason and the sophists will be written in the stars, shivery and awkwardly built. The Neanderthals have objected to being seated with lower lifeforms, and have befriended the Yeti. Should the dakinis stay, they need endure the vicious harpies with their pageboy bobs, Pokemon-pesky, blank stares and tight fists in an ineffectual vanity and vacuity. "Walk away from the two-faced double-dealing," Mani says to the seven dakinis, jumping through their hoops to get to his version of an Anglo-Saxon nirvana.

100 Words or Less

൰

Fiction is experimentation; when it ceases to be that, it
ceases to be fiction.

John Cheever

The Beginning
Viccy Adams

As the bird flew away, Annie wondered if she would always be alone and hungry. When the last of the leaves blew out of the trees, Annie swam in the fish-empty lake until her fingers purpled. A tent appeared on the hillside; Annie licked her lips and started walking.

Inmate
Nick Boreham

It was a cold Saturday morning in April. She sat strapped to a chair in the Essex market place, her head in a scold's bridle, the wind flapping her nightdress against her bare legs. She was about sixty. On the pavement in front of her, a bowl contained a boiled potato and a spoonful of mushy peas. Next to her there was a placard: Can A Human Being Exist Like This?

Exit
Brindley Hallam Dennis

He pushed his way to the back of the house.

I'm going outside for a smoke, he told her.

Light from the bay-window spilled over his shoulder. He shrugged it off, strode to the gate, out across the road, into the field.

Here in darkness, where light from the window had not followed, and the lights of the town did not reach, and there was no moon, he smoked his cigarette.

Silence.

The glow of his cigarette faded. He looked across towards the house, beyond the wilderness of grass. Blood pulsed in his ears, clicks of metal turning.

The Trouble with Robots...
Benjamin Judge

Is their insistence on wearing silly hats. There are times when a fez just isn't acceptable head wear. Try telling that to a robot!

The one that arrived this morning had a top hat on that was about three foot tall. He looked like a metal Cat in the Hat. He stayed about twenty minutes; dismantled the vacuum cleaner, ate a couple of vases and said something unforgivable to my cleaner. Bloody British Robot Corporation.

One of those vases had a picture of Bradley Walsh on. You can't just find them in the shops you know.

Convert, Perceive
Sam Porter

There was a thin, balding man who liked to make simple things complicated. Nice became nasty. Kind became selfish. He said short people were stumpy, tall people gangly, but he loved his I.T. technician, said he was a 'wonderful little man'. Others heard this and said, "Aren't Canadians lovely?"

One day, the I.T. technician made a mistake and I know this because the balding man shouted, "That stupid fucking little Indian. That stinky, nasty, Indian midget wiped my files."
See, to him, it wasn't a mistake, but sabotage.

Miranda in Red
(Inspired by Krzysztof Kieslowski's Version of *The Tempest*)
Hila Shachar

Prologue: a condensed tempest, Miranda in a bob, red coat swinging. She turns a scattered visage. He asks, what is a tempest? Red not blue, a violent restless unkempt minus. I will corrode you.

172

You, who I cannot see through. Swathed and cradled, you turned opaque and said, I'm blue.

So I tore you up and said, this one will do. You murdering myth, a shipwrecked bride of salinity. Princess, (skin crisp, sweating fog), listen.

Epilogue: she answers, Shakespeare! Good old chap. You were on to a thing or two.

Ah, you.

Chiller
Stephen R. Smith

June lifted the freezer lid and tossed a handful of photographs inside.

"You said 'Fuck me if I'm lying'?" She met his stare, watched his confidence melt away.

"I could untie your hands so you could look," she leaned closer, "but I won't."

As the freezer lid dropped she added, "You're fucked now, aren't you?"

Author Biographies

CB

Please visit our website for more information about the authors
www.unboundpress.com

Viccy Adams

Viccy Adams is currently completing her Creative Writing PhD at Newcastle University, funded by the AHRC. She is addicted to reading fiction, drinking tea, and scribbling notes on any paper or paper-related product close to hand when an idea comes into her head. Read more about her work on www.vsadams.co.uk.

Nick Boreham

Nick Boreham lives in Stirling, Scotland. His short story 'Thirdness' appeared in the *Aesthetica Creative Works Annual 2009* and his poem 'Surf Orphan' in the *2011 Annual*. Other poems have appeared in *Equinox* and *Poetry Scotland*.

Christina Brooks

At 55 and after an accident, Christina Brooks could have been forgiven if she had just sat back and relaxed. But instead, she is fulfilling her ambition to write. The pleasure and rewards that this new found pursuit have given her far outweigh the traumas of the last few years. In short, writing has been a blessing.

Joanna Campbell

Joanna Campbell writes short stories all day at home in the Cotswolds, with three cats and occasional bowls of cereal for company. She has been published in various magazines and anthologies. In 2010, she was shortlisted for the Fish, Bristol and Bridport Short Story Prizes.

Kurt Caswell

Kurt Caswell is the author or two books of nonfiction: *In the Sun's House: My Year Teaching on the Navajo Reservation*, and *An*

Inside Passage, for which he won the 2008 River Teeth Literary Nonfiction Book Prize. He teaches creative writing and literature in the Honors College at Texas Tech University.

Ian Crockatt
Ian Crockatt's last two poetry collections were BLIZZARDS OF THE INNER EYE (Peterloo Poets, 2003) and SKALD(Koo Press 2009). A selection of his translations of Rilke's poems is due from Arc Publishing this year. He is currently translating Old Norse court poetry as part of a PhD with Aberdeen University.

Brindley Hallam Dennis
Brindley Hallam Dennis' novella, *A Penny Spitfire*, has just been published by Pewter Rose. In 2010 Unbound Press released *That's What Ya Get!*. BHD has won several literary prizes and awards. In 2008 he received the degree of MLitt from Glasgow University, and currently teaches Creative Writing at Cumbria University.

Max Dunbar
Max Dunbar was born in London in 1981. He recently finished a full-length novel and writes regular criticism for *3:AM Magazine*. He is Manchester's regional editor of *Succour* magazine, a journal of new fiction and poetry. Max lives in Manchester and can be contacted on max.dunbar@gmail.com.

Wanda Ernstberger
Wanda Ernstberger's fiction has appeared in *Spilling Ink Review* and *Aphelion*, and her YA short story will be published by Etopia Press in spring 2011.

John G Fainella
John G. Fainella writes about growing up. He has travelled across Europe, and researched comparative quality of life through extended stays in Montreal, Milan, and Larino. To his literary credit are ebooks, essays, and stories about, and for children. His formative experiences were in Antrodoco, Italy, and in Calgary, Canada.

David Francis
David Francis has produced two albums of songs, one of poems, and a chapbook of lyrics and drawings. In 2008 *NYCBigCityLit* published his article 'Utterance and Hum: The Difference Between

Poem and Song.' David has a new album due for release in 2011. www.davidfrancismusic.com.

Dorothy Fryd

Dorothy Fryd is a writer who teaches Creative Writing at Kent University. Her poetry and fiction has been published in *BRAND Literary Magazine*, *Forward Press*, *Momaya Press*, *Educating Kenyan Orphans*, *WordAid*. She was Canterbury Poet of the Year in October 2009 and was shortlisted for the Bridport 2010 Poetry Prize.

Wayne Lee Gay

Wayne Lee Gay recently completed the Ph.D. in creative writing at the University of North Texas, where he currently teaches in the English Department. He won first prize in the 2010 Saints and Sinners short fiction contest and was the winner of the 2010 Frank O'Connor Short Fiction Award.

Dylan Gilbert

Dylan Gilbert's writing has recently appeared in *The Westchester Review*, *Slow Trains*, *Red Fez*, *Word Riot*, and other literary journals. He lives with his wife and son in New York's Hudson Valley.

Alan Gillespie

Alan Gillespie won his first poetry competition at the age of ten, for a verse entitled 'To a Baked Potato'. He works for a slightly evil corporation and studies Creative Writing at Glasgow University. His fiction appears online and in print and he is joint editor of the online journal, *From Glasgow to Saturn*.

Louise Halvardsson

Louise Halvardsson was born in Sweden in 1982, but now lives in Brighton. Her award-winning debut novel, *Punk industrial hard rocker with attitude*, was published in Sweden in 2007. Her first English novel, *Replacing Angel*, is in progress. She also writes short fiction, and performs poetry under the name Lou Ice. www.louisehalvardsson.blogspot.com

Gill Hoffs

Gill Hoffs, 32, gained a Psychology degree at the University of Glasgow before working throughout Britain with children with a variety of needs. She now lives in Warrington with her husband and son, Angus, and writes whenever a three-year-old and migraines allow. They are teaching Angus to swim.

Steve Howe

Steve Howe is currently in his final year at Goldsmiths College, University of London, studying Media and Modern Literature, where he is also Sports Editor for the University newspaper *The Leopard*. When not in the UK, he can be found teaching English abroad to a classroom of bewildered students.

Benjamin Judge

Benjamin Judge lives in Littleborough. He writes stories in which unusual things happen. His blog is called 'Who the Fudge is Benjamin Judge?' He is allergic to penicillin.

Simon Kewin

Simon Kewin writes fiction, poetry and software, although usually not at the same time. His work has appeared in numerous magazines and anthologies. He lives in the UK with Alison and their two daughters Eleanor and Rose. He blogs about writing at http://spellmaking.blogspot.com.

Kirsty Logan

Kirsty Logan is a writer, editor, teacher, book reviewer, and general layabout. Her short fiction has been published in around 80 anthologies and literary magazines, and broadcast on BBC Radio 4. She has a semicolon tattooed on her toe. Say hello at kirstylogan.com.

Helen McClory

Helen McClory was born and raised in various parts of Scotland both rural and urban. She currently walks dogs for a living on the streets of New York City, while writing a novel of immigrant despair, elation and desertification in her and her husband's tiny studio.

Moy McCrory

Moy McCrory was born in Liverpool of Irish parentage; her fiction has identified her critically as an Irish writer. Author of three short story collections and a novel, her first collection was short listed for the Dylan Thomas Award. Creative non-fiction is a new departure for her.

Caroline Moir

Caroline Moir has lived on four continents, attended nine schools, studied at five universities. A sometime vicar's wife, she is a Creative Writing PhD student at Glasgow University, has published a number of short stories, written and produced street theatre, and is, mostly, resident in Kendal, 'Gateway to the Lakes'.

Christina Murphy

Christina Murphy's writing appears in a number of journals, including, most recently, *ABJECTIVE*, *A cappella Zoo*, *PANK*, *Word Riot*, *Fiction Collective*, and *LITnIMAGE*. Her work has received two Editor's Choice Awards, Special Mention for a Pushcart Prize, and the 2011 Andre Dubus Award for Short Fiction from Words and Images.

Kirsty Neary

Kirsty Neary is a student and writer whose first novel, *The Stately Pantheon*, was published in 2009. She also takes photographs, makes films and performs spoken-word at events and festivals across the country. She would get a lot more done if her cat wouldn't insist on sitting on the keyboard.

Julia O'Byrne

Originally from Toronto, Julia O'Byrne now attends law school at McGill University in Montreal. Writing, travelling, reading, and baking are some of her favourite things to do. Julia keeps a blog (saralytton.blogspot.com) where she writes about all sorts of different things.

Valerie O'Riordan

Valerie O'Riordan has an MA in Creative Writing from the University of Manchester. She placed first in the 2010 Bristol Short Story Prize and has been shortlisted for the Bridport Prize for flash fiction. She's working on her first novel.

Carly Pluckrose

Carly Pluckrose grew up in London. Her work has been shortlisted for the Flash 500 Fiction competition and was a runner up for the Chapter One International Short Story competition 2010.

Sam Porter

Sam Porter finds inspiration in her experiences living and travelling overseas. In her work she explores the issue of culture and its impact on human interactions. She mainly writes short fiction and poetry. She currently lives in the UAE and teaches English for her day job.

Kerry Ryan

Kerry Ryan is a novelist, short story writer and creative writing tutor. She recently completed a PhD in English at the University of Strathclyde and now lives in London where she teaches, writes and works as an editor for a charity and for *3:AM Magazine*.

Beryl Sabel

Beryl Sabel writes compulsively but intermittently. Joining Felixstowe Scribblers has provided some necessary discipline. At present Beryl is three-quarters of the way through a novel based on the lives of her immigrant Jewish grandparents in the East End in the early 1900s.

Hila Shachar

Hila Shachar is an Honorary Research Fellow within the Department of English and Cultural Studies at The University of Western Australia, and writer for The Australian Ballet and *Desktop Magazine*. She is the author of the forthcoming monograph, *Cultural Afterlives and Screen Adaptations of Classic Literature: Wuthering Heights and Company*, Palgrave Macmillan, 2012.

Marc R Sherland

Marc R. Sherland: Humanist, performance poet, writer/organiser. Competition: 2006 National 'Glasgow 2020'; 2008 Erskine Writers' President's Cup; 2009 Castles in the Air; 2010 E.W. winner short story. 2007 & 2009 Glasgow Hidden City poet. Ambassador: Federation Writers (Scotland); Secretary: Scottish Association Writers; Chairperson: WoSLA, Workers Educational Association. Facilitator: Larkfield Writers'; Word Factory; Write Attitude Group; Glasgow Writing Group.

Stephen R Smith

Stephen R. Smith is an avid programmer and technophile, founder of a successful software development and consultancy company and curator of and staff writer for 365tomorrows.com.

Kathrine Sowerby

Kathrine Sowerby has a background in Fine Art and lives in Glasgow with her partner and three children. She is working on her second novel, *The Mast*, and a collection of poems called *River Room*.

Bob Tomolillo

Bob Tomolillo began his career during the burgeoning of the print workshops in the late sixties. A faculty member at the F.A.W.C. in Provincetown, MA and member of the Boston Printmakers since 1983, his lithographs are included in collections here and abroad. In 2009 he was the co-winner of the first Dayton Arts Museum International Peace Prize for his "Think Peace" poster.

Emilie Vince

Emilie Vince is an East Anglian writer and artist with a fascination for representing internal and external realities. Her prose poem 'norwich spring' is part of her new collection which deals with changing relationships, set amongst the East Anglian landscape and its developing seasons.

Lynne Voyce

Lynne Voyce lives in Birmingham with her husband and two daughters where she teaches English in an inner city comprehensive. Her work has appeared in magazines, online and in anthologies. She has been placed in, and won, many competitions. She continues to write short stories and is working on her first novel. She enjoys TV comedy, celebrity gossip and shopping.

Mark Wagstaff

Mark Wagstaff was born by the North Sea and has lived mostly in London. Since 1999 he has been lucky enough to have around fifty short stories published. Mark's most recent novel *In Sparta* – a story of radicalism, conformity and terror – is available now. See www.markwagstaff.com for details.

Mary Wilson
Mary Wilson has worked as a journalist, writer and editor in Southern Africa and the UK. She lives in Cambridge and Cape Town.

Simon Wroe
Simon Wroe is a writer and journalist based in London. He is currently working on a novel.

Desmond Kon Zhicheng-Mingdé
Desmond Kon Zhicheng-Mingdé has edited more than ten books and co-produced three audio books, several pro bono for non-profit organizations. Also working in clay, Desmond sculpts commemorative ceramics, these works housed in museums and private collections in India, the Netherlands, the UK and the US.